I have personally used, shared ~~~~ ~~~~~~~~~~~ Thought Field Therapy for nearly 15 years. I've seen it help my clients move past their fears, heal their traumas and reach their dreams. I learned the depth of healing possible when he helped me release severe pain from a physical issue and TFT has been a true blessing to so many in this world.
—Jack Black, www.mindstore.com

"One of those remarkable instances of the effectiveness and the instantaneous affect of informational medicine I heard about recently and it had to do with this system called Thought Field Therapy, which is an energy psychology that supposedly heals and changes negative thoughts around us. And the theory is negative thoughts hang around us, it's almost like a net, and they affect bodily systems.

They used this system in Kosovo with survivors of the war in former Yugoslavia. These are families who've been severely traumatized because the policies of ethnic cleansing were to kill half of a family just so the survivors would be demoralized. So they took a group of people who had severe Post Traumatic Stress Syndrome who would have required years and years and years of talking cures and medicine. All that sort of conventional thinking and they gave them Thought Field Therapy and, to a person, this is 100% of the people in this study, were made virtually, instantly better to the point where they were laughing, joking. They were healed completely from this trauma. Even the practitioners of Energy psychology were blown away by the power of this modality, but this just gives us one small example of the power of using information as medicine"

—Lynne McTaggart, The Living Matrix, November 2009

"When I observe a number of suffering patients who did not respond to our usual treatment modalities, suddenly get better after TFT treatments are given, I don't need a double-blind controlled study to tell me the value of TFT."

—James Mckoy, MD Chief, Pain Clinic
Chief Rheumatology Services Assistant Chief,
Neuroscience Department, Kaiser Permanente
Hawaii region

"What's fascinating about TFT is it's quick, painless and it's success rate is almost unheard of in the field of mental health in any type of treatment over this whole century."

—Shad Meshad, President, National Veterans Foundation
Founder and Author of the National Vet Center Program

Florence Nightingale once said, "I think one's feelings waste themselves in words; they ought all to be distilled into actions which bring results". I understand this to mean, I should defy precedent and try anything that may improve patient care. I found Thought Field Therapy to be the best action to bring about astonishing results for patients and staff.

—Phyll Robson
RN, RNT, Dip. BC, MIC, TFT Adv
Emotional Support Specialist
North Cumbria University Hospitals NHS Trust
Carlisle, Cumbria. UK.
TFT and Developing countries

"I used Roger Callahan's Five Minute Phobia Cure decades ago when I was launching my career. It eliminated my fear of public speaking so I could move on to live my dreams, appear in movies, on TV, and on stage. Now this inspiring book proves that TFT helps others live their dreams of success and abundant wellness, too. It's fantastic."

—Dr. Joe Vitale, author The Attractor Factor

The TFT mission to Uganda supported a population suffering severe consequences of conflict and disease. In many cases medical symptoms and medical traumas were ameliorated. Haiti was a particular challenge, six months after the earthquake, in a few days we trained and helped many. Those we trained subsequently let us know that the training had given them strength to cope with the further hurricane and cholera. In both countries, we trained people to help themselves, and pass on some simple therapies.

—Dr Howard Robson MA, MB, BChir, FRCP, FRCPE, TFT Dx
Royal College examiner, Retired Consultant Physician and Cardiologist,
Cumbria, UK

Dr. Callahan, the pioneer and originator of Energy Psychology, in his latest book – Tapping the Body's Energy Pathways has skillfully balanced the art and science of Thought Field Therapy with practical techniques that are applicable to a wide range of disorders. I highly recommend this responsible contribution to both practitioners and the general public.

—Lee Pulos Ph.D ABPP
Author – The Biology of Empowerment

"I have known Roger for over 30 years, originally as his instructor in the 100 hour applied kinesiology course, and later as a colleague. He first published the phenomenon of psychological reversal in the International College of Applied Kinesiology (ICAK) Collected Papers. I then published a study in Human Performance demonstrating how extraordinary that simple tapping correction can be in improving performance. Dr. Callahan's development of the psychological reversal is a wonderful contribution, not only to psychology and chiropractic, but to all fields of study related to the improvement of health and human function."

—Robert M. Blaich, DC,
Author, Your Inner Pharmacy

TFT has become my tool of choice when treating "Life Trauma" or PTSD. As a Certified Trauma Specialist, developer of the "Life Trauma Solutions" program and a TFTdx Practitioner, I have seen life changing improvements to otherwise disabling PTSD issues utilizing TFT. For the various forms of trauma, TFT is a instantaneous way to assist someone to eliminate the overwhelming feelings that are often associated. It is versatile enough to use in our "Life Trauma Solutions" Workshops for professionals and clients alike. I am grateful for the many years of work in this field that Roger and Joanne have shared with us in this book. I highly recommend applying these principles.

—Ronald R. Ringo, Jr. PHD, CTS, TFTdx
U.S. Navy Chaplain, Life Trauma Solutions
Service For Humanity Foundation

Tapping the Body's Energy Pathways

Real People Reveal How
Thought Field Therapy®
Heals Trauma, Anxiety and Disease

by
Dr. Roger Callahan
& Joanne Callahan

A publication of
Callahan Techniques Ltd.

ISBN 13:   978-0-615-43788-0
ISBN 10:   0-61-5437885

Published by: Callahan Techniques Ltd., 47159 Youngs Ln., Indio, CA 92201. Telephone: (760) 564-1008.

This book is available at special quantity discounts to use as promotional tools and premiums, or for use in training programs. For more information, please contact the Special Sales Department by sending an email to: info@rogercallahan.com.

Acknowledgments

The discovery and development of a new mode of healing could not happen or survive without the support of many friends, clients, practitioners and researchers, all willing to step forward and try something new, and see with their own eyes, and report new facts, test new theories and try new methods of improving health.

We wish to thank all of those pioneers and leaders who stepped forward with us, to bring this non-invasive, self-help tool to the world. It is their work over the last 30 years that made this book possible.

Thank you to our families who have been so patient, loving and understanding as they were being tapped on, muscle tested, voice tested and detoxed over the last 30 years of improving and expanding Thought Field Therapy.

We proudly thank our grandson, Ryan Tannascoli for his beautiful drawings of where to tap.

Our office manager, Christine Trautner has helped us keep all the letters, articles and materials we receive daily, in some manageable state and we wish to thank her and Sheila Crouser for their long time assistance, dedication and support to serve our customers.

We wish to thank Dwain Jeworski for his marketing and business skills. No matter how good something is, if you can't get it out to the world, no one will benefit. Dwain is leading our expansion and growth with a brilliant combination of marketing, Internet savvy, and understanding of TFT's potential in the world. With his help, we are reaching more and more every day.

Roger and Joanne Callahan

*To all the Thought Field Therapy practitioners
around the world who have helped hurting and despairing people
recover their lives, this book is dedicated to you.*

Table of Contents

Tapping the Body's Energy Pathways

Introduction

For the past 30 years, a simple technique called Thought Field Therapy has been rapidly healing negative emotions such as trauma and anxiety—and even disease—for people who are desperate to regain wellness and normalcy in their lives.

What started as a simple therapeutic treatment to stimulate the body's own healing systems through the identification of a specific code and then tapping this code on various points of the body—using the same system Chinese acupuncturists do—has become a mainstream therapy accepted by medical doctors, psychologists, alternative healthcare practitioners and even military mental-health personnel.

Thousands of people have recovered rapidly from troublesome disorders like insomnia, gout or tinnitus. Others have eliminated stress, anxiety and phobias such as fear of flying and fear of public speaking—literally within minutes. Still others with life-threatening cancer have completely reversed the disease. Hundreds have regained their lives by curbing addictive urges for nicotine, controlled substances or obsessive behaviors. And those suffering the aftereffects of trauma—warfare, rape, injury or loss—have instantly removed the horrible emotions and feelings tied to that event which previously controlled their lives, sometimes for decades.

But while hundreds of thousands of people worldwide have proven that Thought Field Therapy (or "TFT") is the most effective tool available for rapidly improving one's physical and mental health—surprisingly, millions of consumers still suffering from illness, stress, depression and trauma have yet to even hear of it.

That, we believe, is about to change.

With the stories in this book, you'll see for yourself how other people—perhaps with the same disorder or limiting behavior that you have—have used TFT to instantly calm the stress, eliminate the fears and phobias, erase what's holding them back from success, and begin the process of healing, both physically and psychologically.

You'll read stories from soldiers, housewives, retirees, teachers, sports trainers, doctors, veterinarians and corporate executives. You'll discover how TFT works for babies, athletes, bombing victims, war refugees, teenagers, even horses and dogs. You'll celebrate with stroke victims, heart patients, mothers-to-be, young children and others as they find relief and recovery.

And you'll read stories from the TFT practitioners themselves who, every day, treat clients from all walks of life.

Within these stories, perhaps you'll see a little of your own life—a similar disorder or past trauma or controlling behavior that could be eliminated easily, painlessly and rapidly with TFT.

How Did Thought Field Therapy Come Into Being?

In 1979, as a licensed psychologist in private practice at the time, I was counseling a young mother of two who was terrified of water. In fact, her phobia was so extreme, she was unable to pursue even the most basic activities if they involved water or brought her near to water.

To my great frustration, after a year of using all the traditional therapy methods, my patient "Mary" was no better than before. Sitting outside near my swimming pool one day, she became nauseous from just the thought of the water nearby.

Then I had an idea.

Remembering that the Chinese had used acupuncture for over 5,000 years to stimulate the flow of energy through what they call the body's "meridians" or electrical pathways, I asked Mary to tap a few times under her eye—which I knew was the location of the end point of the stomach meridian.

After several seconds of tapping, Mary exclaimed, "It's gone!" and made a beeline for the pool—bending down to splash water on her face.

Quite frankly, I was dumbfounded.

Yet that night, Mary decided to test her phobia cure further by driving to the ocean in a rare California rainstorm. Wading into the surf until the water reached waist-high, she remained completely free of her fear.

Trying to make sense of what had just happened, I questioned how such an unusual technique could bring about results when it was so contrary to all my traditional training and *especially* when it went against all recognized therapy protocols.

Perhaps the act of "tapping" was somehow influencing the body's fundamental energy system—reorganizing Mary's mental and physical responses to her fear of water (a feat that years of traditional "talk therapy" had failed to accomplish). Or perhaps, as the Chinese use acupuncture to do, this "tapping" technique was somehow unblocking the flow of calming, balancing energy—much like life-giving blood flowing through previously blocked arteries.

Realizing that a stunning discovery had been handed to me, I set about proving the underlying reasons why it worked—and how it could be used with many more patients to resolve many more ailments. I soon discovered that some patients needed *a series of points* to be tapped and that, depending on the problem being treated, one tapping sequence was more effective than others. Before long, I had developed various treatment formulas—not only for different phobias, but for all kinds of disorders and afflicted conditions. My clients were not only getting relief from mental and emotional disturbances, but their physical bodies were healing, too.

And when I discovered that many clients were still suffering the effects—years afterward—from traumas, injuries, love pain or grief they had all but forgotten about, I developed a method for diagnosing the underlying ailment and creating a customized tapping sequence for the individual's resulting physical or mental affliction.

Then I met Joanne, and together we continued to develop and improve the healing power of TFT. Soon, we discovered the role that "energy toxins" played in causing disease and hampering a healing result—foods, products and medications that caused a toxic reaction in the individual. So we created a treatment to neutralize these toxins.

Through it all, Thought Field Therapy has delivered predictable and unparalleled results, often with instant relief—such as in the case of trauma and phobias—or with at least immediate evidence that physical healing has begun.

A Recognized Treatment That's Now Mainstream

Of course, with results like these, the scientific community began to take notice—especially when it became evident that Thought Field Therapy could change the practice of medicine as well as change lives. As we continued to develop tapping treatments for complex disorders and conditions and evolved it into the treatment protocol we call "Thought Field Therapy," researchers continued to study TFT and its effectiveness.

But perhaps no other study established TFT as a treatment worthy of attention as much as the search for a cure for *post-traumatic stress disorder*—or PTSD·—with its horrible symptoms of nightmares, flashbacks, phobias and addictive behavior.

In a first-of-its-kind study, Florida State University professors Charles Figley and Joyce Carbonell committed themselves to finding a cure for PTSD within three years by investigating the "active ingredient" in treatments commonly used to address the disorder. The International Scientific Advisory Committee of Clinical Traumatologists was asked to assemble four teams to study four different treatment modalities: Thought Field Therapy, Trauma Incident Reduction, Eye Movement Desensitization and Reprocessing, and VKD (a form of neurolinguistic programming). Each team spent eight days treating 8-16 clients.

And what were the results?

"Our quest for a possible cure for PTSD and related anxiety disorders," research leader Dr. Charles Figley† wrote us at the conclusion of the study, "led to investigations of every kind of 'talk' therapy. From our preliminary findings, TFT appears to be

---

∗ PTSD is an anxiety disorder with complex, ongoing symptoms that is caused by trauma—an event or situation that causes great distress or disruption.
† Charles R. Figley, PhD was Professor and Director of the Interdivisional PhD Program in Family Therapy at Florida State University at the time.

that cure. Congratulations for such a significant contribution to humanity."

Not only that, but the results were found to endure when test patients were followed-up with six months later.

A Fast, Effective and Enduring Treatment

These findings did not surprise us, as we've known for decades that TFT is effective, fast and pain-free for eliminating the emotional aftereffects of trauma. In fact, we routinely participate in both formal and informal research studies because we know TFT will perform reliably in a clinical setting.

It stands up to scrutiny even as many other treatments do not.

How do we know?

Long before we developed Thought Field Therapy and began using it in our practice, our results were similar to those that other therapists were getting with "established" therapeutic practices. *Dismal.* In fact, Roger was constantly frustrated with his admittedly low percentage of patients helped—and refused to accept the industry norm of only 6% to 8% of patients actually benefiting from treatment.

Once we began to use TFT, however, we could reliably treat patients without fearing a lack of results or a later recurrence of the disorder. And whether the studies today looking into TFT are formal or informal, research shows that TFT works.

Best of all, *it does no harm.*

Now, three decades of research later—and 30 years of field testing with real people—we've refined and enhanced the tapping sequences so that Thought Field Therapy now produces unparalleled and near-instantaneous results. Along the way, we've trained thousands of medical doctors, alternative healthcare practitioners, therapists, social workers, religious professionals, lay ministers, chiropractors, school counselors, aid workers, emergency personnel and other professionals to use Thought Field Therapy in their work.

This book is a compilation of their stories, client results and experiences. Some are fascinating. Others are heartwarming. Still others will amaze and astound you at the almost miraculous healing that TFT accomplishes every day.

Even Everyday People Can Master the Basics

But perhaps the most important stories in this book come from everyday people who decided to take their health and wellness into their own hands and seek to improve it with Thought Field Therapy. While "tapping" is never a substitute for emergency medical care or critical surgeries or treatment, it will astonish you at *what it can do*—even after traditional medical care has given up on finding a cure for what ails you.

As the greater medical profession gradually incorporates Thought Field Therapy as a mainstream treatment, hundreds of cutting-edge practitioners are daily proving its effectiveness in their local medical and therapy offices, as we do.

But interestingly, TFT also works on simple ailments when everyday people use just the standard tapping sequences after having learned them for the first time.

In an impromptu "study" of our own—on the air with millions of radio listeners—Roger appeared on nearly two dozen talk shows and treated 68 random callers for various disorders. Only two callers were not helped. However, nine years later, a TFT practitioner with just one year's training set about replicating the "study" by stepping talk-radio callers through Voice Technology diagnosed tapping sequences for various problems. Across 36 radio shows, he treated 68 people over the phone—the same number Roger had—and successfully got results for 66 of them.

Clearly, TFT works—even for people who have only a modest amount of training in the technique and even for radio listeners who are learning for the first time (by telephone!) how to tap out the healing sequences on themselves.

As you'll read in the stories ahead, many more results are achieved by people who've simply read our books, participated in a teleclass or attended one of our live workshops.

We hope you find the healthy new lifestyle, freedom from illness, and formula for a better future you are looking for in the pages of this book.

—Dr. Roger Callahan and Joanne Callahan

Tapping Into the Source of All Healing

As you read the stories in this book, you'll discover a whole new vocabulary of terms and techniques that will become more and more familiar as you try TFT for yourself—and begin to incorporate tapping into your healthy lifestyle.

But to give you an understanding of these terms—and of the tapping treatment itself—this chapter will introduce you to how tapping works. Of course, our other books and training products have far more detailed information about how to tap for specific ailments, but this chapter will introduce you to the science behind tapping and explain why it is such an effective treatment.

The Human Body Has Its Own Electrical System

For decades, scientists have known that the human body has—in addition to its circulatory system, nervous, digestive and other systems—an *electrical system* that helps the body function by carrying electrical impulses and information to the cells, tissues and organs. Dr. Bjorn Nordenstrom of Sweden scientifically documented the existence of electrical circuits in the body more than 20 years ago. In fact, the foreword to his groundbreaking book on the subject said that the body's electrical circulatory system is not only as complex as the circulation of the blood, but that this electrical system also intervenes in all physiological activity—which includes every function of the body from metabolism to breathing to digestion, reproduction and everything else that makes our bodies operate.

Just like a computer needs electricity and information to operate, your body also needs electricity and information to function properly. To do its job, your body's electrical system is made up of a huge web of major energy meridians, smaller subsidiary lines and individual transfer stations that carry electrical energy *and information*—such as emotions, feelings, cell memory and other kinds of electrically charged impulses.

Because it carries information, your body's energy system also intervenes in and controls the *triggers of negative emotions.*

Of course, Western medicine has only recently recognized and understood the importance of this system. But Chinese physicians have known about it for more than 5,000 years. In fact, they've mapped this system's major energy pathways and established acupuncture points along these pathways to unblock the flow of life-giving, healing energy.

Thought Field Therapy or "tapping" uses these same meridians or energy pathways to correct harmful information— that is, *emotional disturbances* that upset the body's healthy electrical balance.

Tuning Into the Thought Field

Negative emotions such as anger and guilt, feelings you still have after a traumatic event, even adverse reactions to toxic substances can create disturbances or "blocks" along these energy pathways.

Merely thinking about a traumatic past event or current illness activates your electrical system and is a crucial part of being treated with Thought Field Therapy. Remember we said that this energy "force field" in your body also carries thoughts and information? When you "tune into the Thought Field," you're allowing your body's energy pathways to call up all the emotions, feelings and other information associated with the problem to be addressed during treatment. We compare this process to turning the dial on your car radio. If you tuned into a different radio station than the one you wanted to listen to, you would get completely different music, news, talk or information than you're looking for.

Once you have the thought in your mind, you'll next need to determine your level of distress around the problem. This will create a benchmark number for you (or your TFT practitioner) to judge whether your distress is diminishing after a few minutes

---

* TFT never asks clients to re-enact or re-live a past trauma or emotionally disturbing event as other therapy methods do. Not only does this technique fail to help therapy patients get better, it can actually cause further trauma and result in extreme physical and psychological damage.

of tapping. We call this number your Subjective Units of Distress score—or SUD—a term you'll see throughout this book as practitioners talk about their client treatment sessions.

Is your distress extreme or more mild?

You'll want to rate your distress level at this moment, using the Subjective Units of Distress (SUD) scale. On this scale, 10 is the worst you could possibly feel, and 1 indicates absolutely no trace of upset.

Is thinking about the problem really necessary?

Yes! We have found that the mind must be attuned to the problem being treated in order for the treatment to have any effect. Clinical psychologists have long known that thoughts of a past trauma or current ailment generally have a profound effect on a person's emotional state. But even though you'll likely experience anxiety or other emotions along with your thoughts, it's an important element in healing. And if you're in a situation of suffering that's in progress—such as an ongoing illness or withdrawal from an addiction—your mind is automatically attuned to the problem, and no special effort need be made.

Tapping Sequences for Various Ailments

Once you have the thought firmly in your mind, it's time to begin tapping. Over the last 30 years, as we developed tapping sequences for various ailments, we identified a handful of tapping points on the body that are part of the most common tapping sequences. These are points along the body's energy pathways that access the system and correct the information it holds.

What does the tapping do?

We believe it provides an external source of information in the form of coded energy which—when done correctly, at the right spot, in the specific order, with the mind tuned to the problem being treated—balances the energy and removes blocks in a particular energy pathway in the body which is suffering from a deficiency or imbalance.

Take a look at the pictures of a face and hand on the next page. You'll see the tapping points identified in these diagrams.

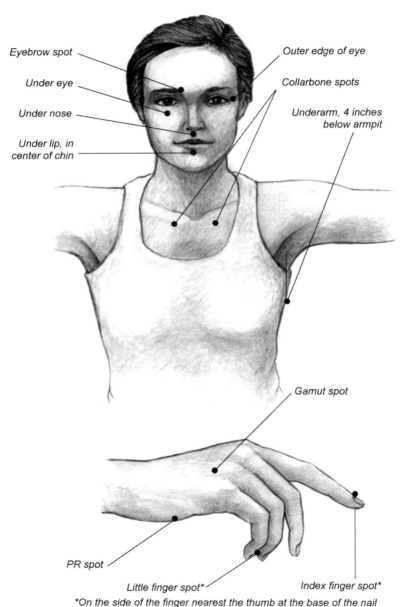

Eyebrow spot

Outer edge of eye

Under eye

Collarbone spots

Under nose

Underarm, 4 inches below armpit

Under lip, in center of chin

Gamut spot

PR spot

Little finger spot*

Index finger spot*

*On the side of the finger nearest the thumb at the base of the nail

Drawing by Ryan Tannascoli - www.ryantannascoli.com

Treatment sequences involve tapping the points in a predetermined order—firmly enough to put energy into your system, but not nearly hard enough to hurt or bruise yourself. Typically you'll tap five times at each point. Under certain circumstances, you'll tap as many as 50 times at a single point, depending on the ailment or energy block involved.

Each tap will stimulate a specifically defined point along one of the body's energy pathways—introducing outside energy and turning it into electrical impulses which have a direct and positive impact on the "thought field" you maintain during treatment.

What does a tapping "treatment" look like? Take a look at the sequence below for trauma. (You can watch videos of treatments for nearly a dozen other ailments for free at our website.) Plus, our other books and detailed training programs will teach you tapping procedures just like this for more complex problems:

TFT Treatment Steps for Trauma

When you do this treatment, remember to tap firmly enough to put energy into your system, but not nearly hard enough to hurt or bruise yourself. Refer to the diagram at left for the exact locations of the treatment points. The simple tapping sequence given here is the only one that most people need for trauma. However, if your traumatic upset combines trauma with anger, rage or guilt that was not resolved with this treatment, our online videos will step you through additional treatment points for these additional emotions.

1. Think about the upsetting event and rate your degree of upset you feel *right at this moment* while thinking about it on a scale of one to ten, where "1" means that you are free of all traces of the upset, and "10" is the most upset you could possibly be. Remember that it is not necessary for you to try to make yourself any more upset than you already are, since this treatment does not require you to painfully relive your experience.

---

* Visit www.rogercallahan.com/pathways for free videos and other tapping resources.

2. Using two fingers, tap five times on the beginning of the eyebrow above the bridge of the nose.

3. Tap five times under your eye about an inch below the bottom of the eyeball, at the bottom center of the bony orbit, high on the cheek.

4. Tap under your arm five times. This point is about four inches directly below the arm pit, even with the nipple on a male or the center of the bra on a female.

5. Find the next point, called the collarbone point. Take two fingers of either hand and run them down the center of the throat to the top of the center collarbone notch, about even with where a man would tie his tie. From this point, move straight down one inch and then go to the right one inch. Tap this point five times.

6. Now do the nine "gamut" treatments. To locate the gamut spot on the back of the hand, make a fist with one hand. This causes the large knuckles to stand out on the back of the hand. Place the index finger of your other hand in the valley between the little finger and ring finger knuckles. Draw your index finger backward about one inch, towards your wrist. This is the "gamut point." Tap this point continuously while going through each of the nine procedures below:

    1. Keep your eyes open.
    2. Close your eyes.
    3. Open your eyes and point them down and to the left.
    4. Point your eyes down and to the right.
    5. Whirl your eyes in a circle in one direction.
    6. Whirl your eyes in a circle in the opposite direction.
    7. Hum a few bars of any tune (more than one note).
    8. Count aloud from one to five.
    9. Hum the tune again.

    While this procedure may sound odd, the various eye positions seem to influence areas of the brain related to the problem in question. Additionally, humming and counting alternately stimulates the right and left sides of the brain.

Remember to keep tapping the gamut spot while doing all nine steps. If you have a disability that prevents you from doing any of the eye movements (for example, blindness), it is not a problem, you can just imagine doing the eye movements while tapping the gamut spot. If you are in a public place and unable to hum and count aloud, you can imagine humming and counting and this usually works just as well.

8. Now, repeat steps 2-5: Tap the eyebrow point (step 2); then tap under your eye (step 3); tap under your arm (step 4) and tap your collarbone point (step 5).

9. Rate your degree of upset again on a scale of 1 to 10. Remember that when you rate your upset, you should rate it according to how you are feeling *right at this moment,* not how you think you might feel in the future. At this point, you will notice one of three things:

   a. Your upset will be at a "1" (completely eliminated) or a "2" (just a slight trace of it left). In this case, end the treatment by doing the floor to ceiling eyeroll. To do this, tap the gamut spot (the same spot described in Step 6) and with your head level, point your eyes downward looking at the floor. Slowly and steadily (taking about 6-7 seconds) roll them up towards the ceiling. This treatment will typically bring you from a "2" to a "1"—or stabilize your "1" leaving you completely free of your upset.

   b. If the number has dropped at least two points, but is not down to a "2" or lower, repeat the treatment (steps 1-9).

   c. If there is a change of only one point (if you originally rated your upset at a "7" or higher) or if you experienced no change, do the following treatment to correct for *psychological reversal* (more about this in a moment). Tap the outside edge of your hand about mid-way between the wrist and the base of the little finger. It's the same spot that would be the point of impact if you were to deliver a "karate chop." After tapping the outside edge of your hand, *repeat steps 1-9 above.*

10. As long as your degree of upset continues to drop two points from a rating of "7" or above or one point from a rating of below "7," continue to repeat the treatment. If at any point, the number you get is unchanged (for instance, you dropped on the first round from a "7" to a "4," but when you repeated the treatment, you stayed at a "4"), tap the "karate chop" spot described in Step 9 for mini-psychological reversal and then repeat the treatment (steps 1-9).

Wow, That Was Easy

As you can see from the above sequence, a TFT tapping procedure is relatively easy, involves no invasive needles or other instruments, doesn't require office visits or embarrassing tests—and is quick to self-administer (or administer to someone else who is unable to do so themselves).

Plus, as you'll soon discover, the standard tapping sequences we've developed and honed over the past 30 years work well for most people. Occasionally, a TFT practitioner may need to create a unique tapping sequence for your specific problem.

Step 9: Correcting for Psychological Reversal

Have you ever noticed times when you are especially hostile, negative and nasty, and you don't know why? In sports, have you ever experienced a "slump" where your body and mind just don't seem to work right, no matter how hard you try? Have you ever suffered in a state of negativism, defeatism, hostility, hopelessness, helplessness, being super-critical, tending to see only the downside of things, or an obsession with the negative aspects of life?

Though you may be aware of these negative patterns, you may feel helpless to stop the behavior. It might even seem as if your willpower is suspended. Because no matter how well you realize that what you're doing is stupid and self-destructive, you seem to be temporarily helpless in doing anything about it.

This mysterious behavior is called *psychological reversal.*

And sometimes, though Nature may prefer to just heal or eliminate the illness or disorder you're also suffering from, psychological reversal gets in the way. A condition that would normally heal simply does not.

Unfortunately, the presence of psychological reversal not only blocks natural healing, it also blocks otherwise effective treatment from taking effect—whether the treatment is Thought Field Therapy, surgery, physical therapy, medication or other remedies. In fact, it's actually *impossible* for you to get better.

Not only that, but psychological reversal can be specialized (affecting only certain areas of our life) or it can be massive (affect most areas of our life in a negative way).

Interestingly, we've found that many high achievers are held back from further success by the problem of psychological reversal. It's not a fear of success, which is so commonly believed, but rather a psychological barrier that is raised as achievement increases. Almost like the sound barrier that supersonic aircraft encounter, psychological reversal holds them back. And when it comes to addiction, we found the incidence of psychological reversal is higher among addicts than for any other group.

Correcting for psychological reversal, on the other hand, jump-starts the normal healing and recovery process, and allows treatment of all kinds to work. Step 9 in the trauma treatment above, therefore, is *not part of the trauma treatment itself,* but merely a correction for psychological reversal which will enable the trauma treatment to work.

Repeated observations in thousands of instances tells us that the effects resulting from psychological reversal are regular, lawful, and predictable—much like the laws of physics or chemistry. That's why we routinely include a correction for psychological reversal in every tapping sequence for every type of affliction. It simply doesn't make sense to do a treatment when success may be blocked by the phenomenon of reversal.

About the TFT Practitioners You'll Meet in These Stories

Many people discover after finding relief with TFT that they want to take additional training and apply tapping to many more areas of their lives. If this describes you, you'll find dozens of tapping seminars every year around the world conducted by us and our partner trainers.

But what if you feel the need to visit a professional practitioner for more complex situations you are facing?

That's when you'll be happy to meet the trained therapists, doctors, counselors, and other practitioners who've decided to make TFT an active part of their practice. In the stories you'll read over the next 12 chapters, you'll meet many of these professionals as they work with clients and bring about miraculous results. They are dedicated and caring individuals who can help you. You'll find a directory of them—in cities around the world—at our website: www.rogercallahan.com/pathways.

Many have taken more advanced, diagnostic level training and can create customized tapping sequences for complex problems you are facing.

Chapter One:
Tapping Away Fear, Anxiety and Stress

According to Jerrold S. Greenberg—professor of public health at the University of Maryland and the author of *Comprehensive Stress Management*—medical researchers say 95% of all disease and illness is caused by stress.

But what is stress, really?

For most people, stress is a bad day at the office, a fight with their spouse, an out-of-control teenager, bumper-to-bumper traffic on the drive home, financial upheaval—plus a myriad of other emotionally charged disturbances that overtax our nerves.

But while those kinds of stress points are real and obvious to everyone, other sources of stress aren't so obvious—or even based in reality. Fear, anxiety, mind-chatter, anticipating disaster, excessive worry and other ongoing, generalized anxiety can be even more harmful to the body than an individual incident that causes stress on a one-time basis.

Why?

Because when the body feels stressed, regardless of the reason, it triggers its own "fight or flight" response—that built-in automatic mechanism that helps humans escape real dangers. Millions of years ago, this acute stress response helped us escape saber-tooth tigers; today, it works the same way to help us face less life-threatening situations.

When the fight-or-flight response is activated, the heart rate speeds up, breathing accelerates, blood is forced away from non-essential activity (such as digestion) into the muscles to prepare us to flee—and hormones such as adrenaline and cortisol flood our bodies, readying it for physical action. We become more alert and hypersensitive to our environment. We may even imagine other potential threats that weren't there before. A vicious circle may form where we see everything through this filter of danger. Fear can become our constant companion.

And with ongoing fear and anxiety, the body's fight-or-flight mechanism is activated repeatedly—along with repeated acceleration of the heart, respiratory system, nervous system and hormones. Unfortunately, as part of this chronic stress response, the body *also* repeatedly shuts down its vital other work—such as cell repair, digestion, processing of waste matter, and toxin removal.

Is it any wonder then, that in this repeated state of "lock-down," disease and illness have an opportunity to form?

Overwhelming medical evidence now shows there is a cumulative danger to repeated and ongoing stress and anxiety. Overactivation of the nervous system can lead to headaches, diabetes, heart disease, sexual dysfunction and cancer—while the buildup of stress hormones in the body can cause chronic fatigue syndrome, depression, allergies, and nearly 100 different autoimmune disorders from asthma to eczema to ulcerative colitis.

By eliminating the underlying stress that causes fight-or-flight, Thought Field Therapy helps reduce the incidence of disease. From mild anxiety to panic attacks to more complex physical and mental illnesses caused by stress, TFT is changing the lives of once fearful, anxious and overwhelmed people.

Their stories are an inspiration and source of hope for anyone suffering the daily effects of stress. Let's take a look at a few of them.

My Life Changes With Thought Field Therapy

Sometimes it's difficult to remember what my life was like before TFT. When I think back, it's almost as if I were a different person. I was continually afflicted with

Acute panic and anxiety	Multiple phobias
High blood pressure	Hormones in disarray
Nervous all the time	Constant chest pain
Extremely overweight	Multiple tumors

I didn't have a life. I couldn't travel anywhere. And even the simplest of tasks, like going to the grocery store, would turn into a nightmare of panic. Most nights were sleepless and fearful—with my jaws clenched and my teeth grinding.

My extreme fear of doctors and dentists meant that I did not take care of my health. In fact, I suffered from ongoing illnesses.

My only "salvation" was food, so I ate for every known reason: Late night eating, television eating, being alone eating, being frightened eating, being financially broke eating, being overwhelmed eating...and the list went on and on. I put on weight and was full of toxins. Any sort of chemical—whether medication, household cleaners, even sending my clothes to the dry cleaner—would set off a panic attack, leaving me gasping for breath and shaking all over.

More than anything else, I just wanted to be normal. I wanted to do the same things everyone else could do. I wanted to get on a plane, go for a drive, meet friends for lunch, sleep at night.

Then I discovered TFT.

The changes in my life have been so remarkable that—to this day—I still cannot express enough gratitude for what this amazing therapy has given me.

My panic attacks are gone along with my phobias—never to return. It's simply wonderful to be free of that burden. My health is fantastic. Actually, it's the best it has been in my adult life. I rarely get sick or even catch cold. I've lost 35 pounds since I no longer need to eat to ease my anxiety.

My fear of dealing with life's basic interactions is gone, too. I engage with people openly now and truly enjoy being me.

I was so thrilled with my own results, I even went on to study and become a TFT practitioner, and have helped hundreds of people over the years find their way back to health with this simple technique.

—*Karen Piccinotti*

* * *

Excessive worry, generalized anxiety and debilitating panic attacks can limit your life and cause other stress-related disorders. Sometimes a toxin is to blame for these attacks. At other times, it's something from our past that causes fear, anxiety and panic.

In this story of lifelong hardship—and panic to the point of fainting—one woman used TFT to finally overcome her past and function normally again.

 ## Panic-Free and Living Life Fully

After experiencing tremendous trauma in my life, I eventually found myself suffering terrible panic attacks. By 1998, I couldn't stand in line at the bank or the supermarket without feeling panic to the point of fainting. I'd panic at the thought of taking the train or bus—feeling trapped by the crush of all those people.

I rarely shared my pain with anyone, but one day, a hairdressing client of mine gave me a voucher for a psychologist who conducted TFT sessions over the phone. A note with the voucher said it would change my life. *If only,* I thought. *If only that would come true!*

I remember feeling strange sitting there on the phone and tapping on myself. *I can't bring up my inner feelings,* I thought. Assuming briefly that it would never work, I finished my phone session and walked outside for some fresh air. How relaxed and at ease my body felt!

Two days later, I went to the bank—expecting that familiar feeling of dread. Amazed, I felt nothing but calm.

For six panic-free years, TFT changed my life.

But, for me, the trauma that originated my panic attacks came back in full force as I suffered a miscarriage and was diagnosed with cervical cancer during another pregnancy—eventually losing my dream of having more children. My father committed suicide. Then when my mother-in-law died tragically, I found myself nearing a breakdown and in yet another state of panic.

Since TFT had provided relief six years earlier, I telephoned my previous TFT practitioner and—again—TFT saved my life.

Even today, it continues to help me function. Unfortunately, I've been recently diagnosed with an extremely rare disorder, *Mal de Debarquement*—a balance disorder distinguished by a persistent sensation of motion, difficulty maintaining balance, extreme fatigue, and difficulty concentrating. Needless to say, the disorder comes with an extra measure of anxiety.

To cope, I practice the Panic/Anxiety sequence every day before work, and it's because of TFT that I still manage to work.

Because of TFT, I've survived over the past year—even with this debilitating illness. My doctors and psychologist are interested in TFT, now that they've seen amazing results in me.

I know that if I didn't have *Mal de Debarquement,* my anxiety would never return. TFT is that amazing. I recommend it to everyone. I even talked two neighbors through the anxiety sequence and they were amazed at the instant results. Thank you, Dr. Callahan for giving so many people the power to heal themselves with this simple technique.

—*Lisa Borg*

* * *

Everyday anxiety, debilitating fear and recurring panic attacks are just the beginning of the stress that TFT can relieve. But what if you or your loved one has fear about a *specific kind* of activity, job duty, interaction with people, or other task that everyday life requires us to complete?

TFT works there, too. Especially if you're a young person who is required to "perform" every day at school, in a sport or when playing a musical instrument. Read what two Ph.D. educators reveal about how they use TFT to help young students overcome classroom anxiety.

TFT for Math Anxiety

Recently we presented "TFT for Math Anxiety" at the Colorado Council of Teachers of Mathematics conference in Denver. While few people outside the classroom have to deal with Math

Anxiety, experienced educators know it's a widespread problem in schools—both for teachers and for their students.

Math anxiety can be indicated by an uneasiness around doing math; avoidance of math classes; feelings of illness, panic, and fear; inability to perform on tests; and lack of progress in tutoring situations. Experts have suggested that high levels of anxiety can reduce short-term memory, reduce the ability to develop permanent new memories, and cause the secretion of cortisol—which has been associated with heart disease, immune disorders, and depression.

Professor Karen Norwood of North Carolina State University has suggested that math anxiety could be caused by negative parent and teacher attitudes toward math, being unprepared, difficulty handling frustration, low self-concept, and being in a class where the focus is on learning math through drill rather than through understanding.

Numerous tests have been developed to measure math anxiety, and many methods have been proposed for teachers to use in order to help students with the condition. Some of them include building student confidence, helping students understand math, and using a variety of interesting teaching methods to teach math. Other methods include helping students apply math in interesting ways, using humor, being enthusiastic about math, making math fun, giving partial credit on tests for process even if the student didn't get the correct answer, fostering positive attitudes toward math, giving immediate feedback, being sincere and caring, not testing the student with the rest of the class, and referring the student to a counselor[†].

While so much has been written to further the knowledge of math anxiety by teachers—and provide relief of math anxiety for students—the condition still exists in schools.

That's where TFT can help.

---

[*] For more details, read *Early Childhood Mathematics* by Susan Sperry Smith (1997). A publication of Allyn & Bacon.
[†] Godbey, C. (1997). Mathematics anxiety and the underprepared student (Descr. Rep. No. 141). Murfreesboro, TN: Middle Tennessee State University.

When we decided to present a session on TFT for Math Anxiety at the educators conference, we knew in advance that difficulty in understanding math concepts—not to mention math exams and math homework—can be extremely traumatic for some students. We started our session by teaching Colorado teachers the TFT tapping algorithm for eliminating the emotional effects of this trauma. We also trained teachers to tap for the many underlying reasons for Math Anxiety such as anger, rage, guilt, and shame—all possible background reasons for math anxiety and the feelings that go with it. Only then did we teach the anxiety algorithm itself to deal with the stress of math anxiety.

After seeing the success of the demonstrations and practicing the algorithms themselves, the teachers that day not only saw the benefits of TFT, they were enthusiastic about using it with their students who have math anxiety. One woman planned to use it with her daughter for test anxiety. Another commented, "I was surprised at how the tapping helped *me* relax!" Still another took a set of handouts for his daughter's therapist—who works with students with ADHD.

—*Jenny Edwards & Jill Strunk, EdD, LP*

* * *

Because TFT works directly with the *emotions* surrounding anxiety, practitioners find their patients and students don't need to have extensive knowledge of psychotherapy or the ability to "sort out" their feelings—or even have mature reasoning, intuition and other thought processes.

For this reason, TFT is ideal for young students. Even younger than that, anxious and fearful *babies* can benefit from the tapping sequences of TFT. Let's take a look.

TFT and Anxiety in Infants

Settling in for the 16-hour flight on my way home from presenting at the Pacific Rim Energy Conference, I had an amusing experience. The huge airliner was filled to capacity, and several families were traveling with infants on board.

When I requested a bulkhead seat so I could stretch out my legs, I had no idea that—during long flights—this section was also used to hang baby beds off the bulkhead. As a result, I found myself surrounded by infants including an adorable baby boy and his family traveling next to me.

Before the flight, I had noticed the parents in the lobby—playing with their happy infant, while awaiting boarding instructions. Unfortunately, by the time we boarded, it was 9:30 p.m. and the babies were already tired and stressed. Of course, when the airplane took off, the crying began.

I expected that.

Yet when the plane leveled off, the cries simply escalated. Mothers and fathers took turns walking their babies around. Nothing worked.

Hoping to help, I turned to my seat mates and told them I thought I could calm their infant. Of course, they didn't believe me. So I went on to explain I had just come from Singapore, where I was teaching energy therapy, and that I was pretty sure it would work on their son.

By this time, they were willing to try anything (and so, I imagine, were the passengers). Tapping on myself to illustrate, I showed them how to tap out the simple anxiety algorithm (eye, arm, collarbone). They did it twice and the baby calmed down immediately. In fact, he was asleep within minutes. Placed in his hanging bed, he slept almost 12 hours. And when he awakened, he remained calm for the rest of the flight.

Another parent had been watching and asked me to show him the same tapping sequence. I treated yet another infant with the same result. Mission accomplished.

Peace was restored.

—Susan Wright

Of course, just like those anxious babies on that 16-hour flight, our anxiety and stress can affect others around us. While we may not know it, often times we project our own fears onto others—seeing danger around them, hovering to prevent disaster, stifling and oppressing our loved ones with our own fear of failure, isolation or impending disaster.

TFT can help everyone in this situation—from the person fraught with anxiety to the friends and family members who must live with them.

When We Project Our Fears Onto Others

In my practice as a homeopathic physician, I work with patients in all kinds of situations. But rarely do I need to work on a family member *first* before my actual patient can get well.

Recently, I used TFT on a near-hysterical woman—the mother of a teenage patient of mine.

The patient—a beautiful and vibrant 16-year old girl—complained repeatedly that her mother didn't trust her. Though the daughter earns good grades, doesn't do drugs, doesn't smoke or drink alcohol—and is well-behaved in other respects—her mother criticized her friends, her grades, her laziness, even her "lack of preparation for life."

The mother, according to my patient, was "half-crazy."

Since there was no father active in her life, I asked my young patient to bring the mother to our next appointment. Not surprisingly, the mother showed up—wizened, bitter, ugly-looking, frantic and fraught.

We talked for awhile about the relationship between herself and her daughter. After a while, I asked the mother if she would like a treatment for her fears about her daughter hanging around the wrong friends, going downhill in school, not being prepared for life, being lazy, fighting with the mother, growing away from the mother (who has no one else), suffering poverty in the cruel world alone (like the mother), and about her daughter being badly prepared for life (for which the mother feels guilty).

When she agreed, I simply asked her to think about her daughter and bring together in her mind all of her concerns until they were unbearable.

Within seconds, she had visibly blanched.

Detecting a lifetime of fear in this woman, I began the treatment using the simple TFT sequence for phobia. Next, I used the technique for psychological reversal—followed by a simple affirmation statement and the instruction to roll her eyes upward, then downward.

Suddenly, she gasped, "Oh! What happened to me!?"

"What are you feeling?" I asked calmly.

"I feel a big warmth coming through my body. And I'm dizzy," she replied with fervor.

As a healthy flush began to spread over her body, her face relaxed and her demeanor changed completely. She was like another person altogether, weeping with joy—as though something dark had moved from her body, leaving behind her healthy spiritual self in full bloom.

—*Norma Gairdner, HD*

* * *

Whether the stressed and anxious person is middle aged, elderly, a young student or an infant—doesn't matter! TFT works on the energy pathways of the body to calm the feelings, emotions and fears that underlay stress and anxiety.

Not surprisingly, these energy pathways exist in other mammals, too. This makes sense, since the body is essentially an electrical power station—moving energy and electrical impulses throughout the body to run its various functions.

Animals possess these same electrical pathways, which allows TFT to work just as well on dogs, horses and other mammals. Like other "alternative" treatments, TFT has been used on racehorses, show dogs, and everyday pets for decades.

One of our favorite stories is this one—about a TFT practitioner who helped an anxious and previously mistreated horse reconnect with people who were there to help her.

" The Algorithmic Horse

While visiting a friend's farm recently, the farmer's daughter shared with me the story of her 7-year-old mare, who was extremely fearful of people—and especially hostile to men. The horse had been mistreated by its previous male owner. By now, it needed veterinary treatment to trim its hooves—which were overgrown and causing the horse extreme discomfort.

Unfortunately, the local veterinarian is a man and couldn't get near the horse, even to examine it. Not wishing her mare to be sedated, the farmer's daughter shared with me her dilemma.

Could TFT help calm this anxious horse, I wondered?

I explained briefly about TFT, then asked the daughter to stroke the horse's forehead, and tap gently under its eye. I then asked her to tap behind the horses foreleg (as close to where I imagined the arm point would be), then tap the horse's chest—as close to the collarbone as she could get.

Since it was impossible for me—a man—to get near the horse initially, I asked the daughter to tap out the algorithm instead. As she tapped away to my instructions, I could see the horse calming down from a distance. I entered the field and slowly walked to the animal, repeating the algorithm where the daughter left off.

In just a few minutes, the mare was almost asleep.

I asked the farmer's daughter to walk away and leave the field. By then, she was extremely surprised to find the horse calm, receptive and unaffected by her departure—particularly when the mare had not been bridled in any way, nor had I used any treats.

Later, as I walked about the field, the horse followed me, nudging me in the back—her fear of people (and men, in particular) completely resolved. Even another male visitor to the farm that afternoon couldn't change the anxiety-free state of the mare.

Of course, the veterinarian was able to treat her hooves with ease. But getting her to hum a tune while tapping was a different matter entirely!

—Brian Ewart as told to Ian Graham

Valuable show dogs, too, can enjoy the calming benefits of TFT. In this story from an acclaimed Animal Behavior Specialist in Coronado, California, tapping saved one dog's show career—who, after biting a judge and being dismissed from the ring for it, went on to earn his Championship once TFT had given him more confidence with strangers.

 **A Wells Trained Dog**

In one successful experience with TFT, I was retained to work with a Jack Russell Terrier who had been dismissed from the Conformation Ring for growling at and biting the judge when he went over the dog.

Could TFT cure this problem? I wondered.

After some basic obedience training using positive reinforcement, I found the pup only about 80% reliable. By using TFT, I was able to break through that final 20% and he went on to earn his Championship.

I started with desensitizing handling, then had strangers go over him while he was on a table. When he showed his teeth and growled at them, I started TFT.

At first, the pup was not receptive to the tapping. That is to say, he resisted it. I started by tapping him in the middle of his forehead, a technique I have used for many years (prior to my knowledge of TFT) to calm hyperactive dogs. After getting his attention, I used the eyebrow, under eye, under arm, clavicle, and gamut tapping sequence.

At first he looked surprised, and then he calmed.

After several treatments, the pup seemed to invite the tapping as though aware it was making him feel better. Eventually he was able to be handled without any treatment.

I have used TFT with other dogs including, recently, two Labrador Retrievers who were rescued from very abusive homes. Both dogs were fear-aggressive, lunging, barking, snapping, then retreating. After working with the dogs for several days, gaining their confidence, I had a stranger approach each dog to maximize his trauma. I then applied the treatment, tapping the forehead, under eye, clavicle and sternum. Both dogs calmed noticeably. After several treatments, they were more easily approached.

Additional applications of TFT have been used many times, briefly, when working with students in classes. As I approach the pups, signaling them with calming signals, I then tap them on the forehead, under the eye, and on the sternum or clavicle, whichever is easier to find.

It has been my experience that when TFT is applied in a calm quiet manner, there is usually observable evidence of calming and an increase in the dog's confidence. There is a correlation between the degree of improvement and the dog's previous experiences, some of which have been quite traumatic. Those dogs often require several treatments before improvement is observed.

The most common reasons for lack of success include moving too quickly (i.e., not gaining the dog's trust), interference by the owners, or their unwillingness to continue with the treatments.

I believe TFT works best when the dog has confidence in the person applying the treatment. It should not be tried with a dog who is frightened of everyone and has no "ally" in the room. These dogs are not receptive to any form of treatment, and it is very difficult to tap the appropriate spots. It is best to sit quietly with the dog to gain his confidence, then apply TFT in a calm, non-threatening manner.

The response will be very rewarding.

—*Lee Wells*

* * *

Just like the valuable show dog in the story above, even severely traumatized dogs can benefit from TFT. Imagine fear and anxiety from a dog's point of view. Often times they've been mishandled, abused or put into frightening new circumstances. They may be angry, fearful, lonely. They may not know what's expected of them.

TFT can calm these fears and give a dog more confidence when meeting strangers—or even when moving into a new home.

In this heartwarming story from a TFT practitioner, two fearful rescue dogs respond to the calming influence of tapping—including one who is so dangerous, the practitioner uses the "surrogate technique" of focusing on the patient while tapping out the sequence on her own body.

 ## Easy Tapping Techniques for Uneasy Rescue Dogs

I have been visiting an animal rescue center and recently had the opportunity to work with a dog that was traumatized. She was at the center for re-homing and was lying shivering in her basket. She would not move from it and braced her feet against the side so that it was almost impossible to move her.

As she lay trembling, I talked to her and tapped using the trauma algorithm. I next used algorithms for complex trauma, anger and rage. Gradually she became a little more interested and did not tense her body quite as much. I was able to lift her to a sitting position and then, after some more tapping, she stepped out of her bed and came with me for a walk. It had taken about 30 minutes. She was still very nervous, had her tail between her legs and pulled back when she saw another person or dog.

However, she seemed to enjoy the walk!

The next day, I found her—again—in her basket, trembling fearfully. But this time she picked up her head and looked at me, and even wagged her tail a little. It took 5 minutes to get her to step out of her bed and go outside with me. The next time I visited the center, I saw her running in and out of her outside pen and jumping up to greet people!

After that success, the staff asked me to work with another dog—only a few months old and already biting and snapping.

"He's a challenge," said the staffer. "Be careful of that one."

After listening blithely to advice that I'd have to 'lasso' him by dropping a loop of lead around his neck, I found the dog cowering in the corner behind his bed.

I sat on the floor and focused my attention on him, using surrogate tapping to calm him. Eventually he got up and walked over to me and sniffed my hand. He went away and came back a few times, and I was gradually able to stroke his head and begin touching the tapping points on his head.

He didn't make any attempt to growl or bite, and after a short while I was able to tap gently through the sequence and put a collar around his neck. I took him outside, although he was obviously not used to walking on a lead so I carried him some of the way and sat with him, continuing to tap whenever he seemed uneasy. He yawned the way some people do after a TFT session.

Later, one of the staff tried her own puppy in the dog run with him. And 30 minutes later, she had both puppies on leads on the grass outside the building!

—Jo Cooper

Tapping Away Fear, Anxiety and Stress

You'll find videos that step you through the complete tapping sequences for fear, anxiety and stress at our website:

www.rogercallahan.com/pathways

Chapter Two:
Erasing Trauma and Its Aftermath

Every day, people around the world suffer sudden and unexpected trauma—a serious injury or shock to the body or mind caused by violence or an accident.

And while their *physical* injuries can usually be healed by the body, what is left behind is often worse—an emotional wound, sometimes undetected, that causes a lasting psychological effect or even neurosis* in the patient. Anxiety, depression, a continual feeling of illness, even nightmares and hallucinations—all these can be the aftereffects of an event or situation that causes great distress or disruption.

Experts call this aftereffect *post-traumatic stress disorder.* And not surprisingly, traditional therapy is often used to help patients deal with the trauma and put their lives back together.

Unfortunately, many trauma survivors in more traditional therapy are told they must "re-live" the trauma and re-experience the pain in order to get better. Faced with this horrible choice, such patients often flee from treatment only to continue to suffer the aftereffects. Even most of those who do stay in treatment experience little, if any, relief—and may actually worsen.

For 30 years, TFT has given patients an alternative method to heal from trauma. In fact, based on thousands of stories of healing we receive from practitioners, their patients and clients, TFT often provides relief when all other methods have failed.

How exactly does TFT work to quickly and painlessly eliminate the devastating aftereffects of trauma?

Rather than working with the patient's memory, TFT instead works directly on the brain itself, changing the way in which the brain has compiled information about the traumatic event. In other words, TFT directly affects the coding system the brain uses to store negative emotions.

---

* A mental disorder where patients experience anxiety, obsessive thoughts, compulsive actions, or physical complaints without actual evidence of physical disease. Today, neurosis is more often diagnosed as one of many different and specific "personality disorders."

Compare it to a building that catches fire with people inside—a traumatic event. As hundreds of panicked people flee for their lives, there is confusion, fear, hysteria and disorder on the stairways and near the doors. Emotions are high; the scene chaotic.

TFT rearranges this jumbled mess of information, collecting the person's emotions so the patient is put into a stronger state. They really don't know how they have changed. They only know *they are no longer bothered by the memory.*

Relief happens rapidly—often within minutes as with simple post-traumatic stress disorder. In other cases, where severe injury, disease or other issues are present, healing may take longer.

For so many people, however, TFT provides the first real relief they've seen. Many TFT patients and clients call their healings "miraculous." Even doctors, military medical personnel, psychotherapists and other professional practitioners use TFT as a non-invasive way to help heal the aftereffects of trauma.

Why?

Because unlike more traditional forms of psychiatry, exposure therapy or prescription medication which can actually cause additional trauma, pain and suffering, TFT gets results—yet *does no harm.*

When we combed through our archives to bring together stories for this book, unquestionably the most poignant and moving stories came from people who suffered trauma—becoming injured in a sudden accident, war experience, or other event—only to heal physically, but carry the psychological effects for years.

Read what they say about their initial experiences—and the relief they eventually found with TFT.

 Right Place, Right Time

So much destruction, I thought numbly as we drove our way through police roadblocks and past the rubble and deserted streets of Nairobi. Just days earlier, I'd been training the Sisters of the Carmelite Community and other religious and lay people to use TFT in their work—while 25 minutes away, a truck bomb exploded inside the gates of the U.S. Embassy, demolishing the building and its surrounding neighborhood.

Over 200 people were killed in the blast; another 4,000 were wounded. And although the attack was directed at American facilities, the vast majority of casualties were local citizens including thousands who worked in the 21-story office building next door.

When I had first heard about Thought Field Therapy years earlier, I knew I wanted to learn it for my work in Africa. I give seminars there, and thought that people would benefit from knowing a rapid way to eliminate trauma, physical pain, anxiety, addictions, phobias, and all of the other areas that Thought Field Therapy addresses.

Back then, I didn't know just how much it might be needed.

When the United States Embassy was bombed on August 7th, the Carmelite Sisters went into action. In fact, all during that first weekend of my training, they were absent—away at the hospitals helping victims of the blast. By Monday afternoon, the other people in the training, though interested, were beginning to question Thought Field Therapy. After all, they reasoned, thousands of their fellow citizens had just been through a bombing. Surely TFT wasn't powerful enough to help people with trauma that severe.

I knew that I had to—and wanted to—go to the hospital and work with bombing victims.

As the Sisters and I made our way through the wards of Kenyatta Hospital in downtown Nairobi, I began to realize the severity of the situation. People's faces were filled with stitches. Eyes were bandaged. It would be unthinkable to ask them to tap on their eyebrows and under their eyes (even though Dr. Callahan told me later, in such cases there are equivalent points on the toes). We went from ward to ward. Having already been there for days, the Sisters knew what to do.

When we finally came to a ward in which people had mostly lower body injuries, I went up to one woman lying on her bed, staring into space, and began talking with her. She was in a great deal of pain. Her shoes had been blown off by the blast, and she had walked out of the building. With glass imbedded in her feet, among other injuries, she was on strong pain medication. But since her injuries weren't as severe as others' in the ward, the doctors hadn't had a chance to work on her yet.

When I offered to work with her and described TFT, she replied she would do anything—she was in that much pain. She also couldn't help thinking that another bomb would explode any minute inside the hospital.

"I know it's probably not going to happen," she said, "but I can't get the thought out of my mind."

After first tapping the algorithm to treat her for pain, her SUD—or *subjective units of distress*—came down from a "10" to a "5." It wouldn't go any lower, leading me to conclude that we needed to tap for trauma before the pain would go away.

Of course, on the SUD scale of 0 to 10, her trauma was a "10," yet it easily came down to "0" immediately. After that, we tapped again for pain, and it readily went down to "0."

Bewildered by the transformation, she blinked her eyes and looked at me.

"I've replayed the pictures of what happened during the bombing over and over in my mind, almost without stopping since Friday," she said. "It's really strange, but I'm not doing that any more. I think that I'll be able to sleep tonight."

I told her that—because her injuries hadn't been seen by doctors yet—the pain probably would return, and wrote out what she could do when it did. I told her that the trauma probably wouldn't return; however, if it did, the directions were there for her to follow.

Across the ward, another woman had been watching us.

"I want to be healed, too," she told one of the Sisters.

As I made my way to her bed, I could see pain and distress clearly etched on her face. Her arm was bandaged and her hand was limp.

While she was in terrible pain, she said she was willing to have me tap even on her limp hand if she could experience the changes she had just seen in the woman across the ward.

On the SUD scale she was a "10" for both trauma and pain.

Working on the trauma first, I tapped and it came down fairly quickly to a "0." Then, we worked on the pain, which had already gone down to an "8" after working on the trauma. As she tapped the pain sequence for herself, it went down to "0," too. She began to move her hand—and color flooded back to her face. She smiled and began to laugh.

As I wrote down what we had done, her husband, who had been watching, asked Sister if tapping might help his neck pain.

"Of course," Sister replied.

By now, the first woman was sitting up for the first time since the bombing, eating dinner and talking with her husband. They were smiling and laughing. Her husband told Sister that his wife usually panicked when it was time for him to leave for the night—she didn't want to be alone for fear another bomb might explode. He reported that this evening, for a change, she felt fine about his leaving, and told him that she would see him the next day.

She then told Sister that she had been on extremely high and frequent doses of pain medication, and planned to use tapping to lessen the amount and frequency of the doses.

Back at the training the next day, the Sisters shared what had happened in the hospital. Participants were amazed, and as I did demonstrations with attendees around their trauma related to the bombing, they became believers and launched into the practice sessions with vigor. They even sent friends with extremely difficult cases to me to work with in the afternoons for the rest of the week.

When I originally discovered TFT, I knew I wanted to share it with the people in my seminars in Nairobi. I didn't know just how timely the TFT training would be.

—*Jenny Edwards*

* * *

Undoubtedly one of the worst causes of trauma—war and terrorism can leave lasting scars.

When it became apparent that Thought Field Therapy could help victims of conflict, the ATFT Foundation was formed to provide humanitarian relief, training and education worldwide. Our focus has been trauma relief in the world's most devastated areas. The Foundation has sent teams of trained practitioners to the refugee camps of Kosovo, the genocide victims of Rwanda, as well as to Haiti, Uganda, Tanzania and New Orleans—and to other areas of the globe where political upheaval, warfare and natural disasters create thousands of refugees and homeless who need relief from trauma.

In this next story about how TFT is used in the field, Guy Marriott—who trains British Special Forces in the Congo and provides security for international aid organizations in places like the Sudan, Zimbabwe and Haiti—tells why TFT works so well...and why it's part of his first-response kit on every mission.

 ## The Beat of a Different Drum

Another volley of gunfire drifted up from the valley as I stared at the battered map and mentally logged the tracks and wadis that were still passable in our four-wheel drive vehicles. I was hoping for an easy answer as to which route might offer a rapid and safe evacuation corridor if the fighting got out of hand.

I gazed at the sun tracing its final descent through troubled skies, momentarily transfixed. And once again I found myself considering how much violence the 30-odd people in my care could or even should endure before I would call 'time' and override their desire to stay and help the fifty thousand people that had made it to the refugee camp to the east of us.

There are so many things that you need to consider in a hostile environment: Everything from the skills and abilities of yourself and the people around you to the strategic decisions of rebel leaders.

I often say that working in hostile environments is a lot like white-water rafting...

- You need to be good at reading the water upstream— understanding what kind of rapids you may face and how you're going to deal with the flow.
- You need to be good at paddling in the white water—when you hit them, hostile environments become highly dynamic.

- You need to be good at making the most of your downstream time—after you've paddled the rapids, understanding what you did well and what you need to do better next time.
- And finally, you need to be good at thinking outside the box— to see other options and other possibilities, perhaps getting out of the water and hauling your raft safely past unnecessary risks.

Many of the skills that enable people to operate safely in hostile environments come from the military. Many skills—sadly less often taught—help us understand two-legged mammals.

Operators in this field are often naturally good at sensing their opponent's intention and understanding the software that drives human beings. They may be good at reading people's eyes, or hearing beyond the words that are spoken, or feeling and perceiving things that are somehow there, yet remain invisible.

All situations are invariably different in hostile places and sadly there is often no single 'right answer.' What works safely in one country might be dangerous in another.

I'm lucky enough to have traveled pretty extensively throughout the world and have seen many things that I long to see again—and many things that I never want to see again.

I now divide my time between operating in hostile places and teaching those skills to others. The people I train come from Non-Governmental Organizations (NGOs), government agencies and corporations. The skills we teach include things that you'd expect—like Anti-Ambush Drills, Mine Awareness, Checkpoint Procedures and Surveillance.

Many people are surprised to learn that TFT has a place within our core skills modules. Yes, we really do show TFT to big, rough, soldier-type people! And most, I'm happy to say, really appreciate it—mainly because TFT is highly effective and works for them.

My company, Ground Truth Consulting, runs 5- to 10-day Hostile Environment Awareness Training (HEAT) programs. They are highly experiential and very realistic. We demonstrate the basic TFT trauma sequences for our participants—usually after we've let them experience the shock of capture and hostage-taking for themselves. We demonstrate the impact of trauma on people and we combine TFT with Critical Incident Debriefing techniques.

Many of our government clients were skeptical of TFT at first. However, because our training is realistic and often triggers memories of trauma, we know that the participants— particularly those who have already been through the classic hostile-environment cocktail of fear and trauma on a previous assignment or mission—will actually experience TFT working on their own trauma and get tremendous benefit from it.

I often see post-traumatic stress disorder symptoms being masked by people working in hostile environments—masked by nicotine, caffeine and alcohol. Even in safe training environments, we know that some people will re-experience trauma and stress-induced responses when they undergo realistic training.

All of our training team are qualified medics and—having seen TFT used over the years (even with the most skeptical ex-military types)—they all understand that knowing the TFT tapping sequence for trauma is as essential as carrying a ballistic trauma pack in places where the AK47 rifle is common!

I personally have used TFT all over the world to great effect, on every continent except Antarctica. It's a fantastic tool because it is culturally mobile; it works beyond language—an enormously limiting factor for interventions which use cognitive psychological techniques.

Whether I have used TFT post-earthquake, post-crossfire, post-bombardment or even due to something farther back in time and less obvious, TFT has been a tool that I'm incredibly grateful for.

The last time I used it in a training program was with someone who had been kidnapped from Darfur in Sudan only a month before. They had suffered through mental, physical and emotional violence including being forced to endure mock executions. Another person in the program had been kidnapped 13 years earlier. During both treatments, their SUDs came down to 1 and 2 respectively after just 5 minutes using TFT.

We intend to keep promoting TFT as one of the most valuable tools for teams and individuals working in hostile environments. As I write this, I am thinking about what to pack for my next trip, tomorrow night to Zimbabwe; another country on the brink of violent collapse. One thing that I am grateful for is that I will never forget to pack my working knowledge of TFT.

I'm constantly amazed at what it does and how well it works. Even under fire.

—*Guy Marriott*

* * *

War, famine, earthquakes, floods. These are just some of the traumas that are inflicted upon people living around the world today. But, by far, the threat and violence of war can be the most permanently damaging trauma for those involved—not only for the local populace, but also for those soldiers who are sent to foreign lands to fight these wars.

Many soldiers return from duty suffering Post-Traumatic Stress Disorder—an often disabling condition rife with nightmares, flashbacks, phobias and anxiety.

TFT has proven time and again that it *instantly* relieves PTSD—so much so that military personnel, military doctors, and civilian employees of the military are quietly turning to TFT in a non-official capacity, seeking relief from this mentally crippling disorder.

What do they say about their recovery?

"It's a Distant Memory"

I wish I had Thought Field Therapy when I was sitting in Joint Readiness Training· waiting for the Op Force to attack. I was panicking. It was just a training situation, but I had a hard time coping with that. [The panic] was something I could have treated

---

· According to the JRTC's website, the Joint Readiness Training Center not only conducts tough, realistic, multi-echelon arms training to train leaders to deal with complex situations, it also develops highly proficient, cohesive units capable of conducting operations across the full spectrum of conflict. Training is focused on the current operational environment and counterinsurgency operations. Soldiers come away from the exercise fully capable and prepared to handle situations that may arise in any theater of operations.

myself—just by tapping. Thought Field Therapy has made a major difference in my life. The first time [using] Thought Field Therapy, I thought it was ridiculous. I was full of hate, anger—everything you could think of, I was feeling it. Within 30 seconds, it was gone. I remember it, but it's a distant memory. It doesn't affect me in any way psychologically, emotionally, spiritually, financially—in no way does it affect me any longer. [TFT] is something that I can do anywhere in the world. I have sat in meetings with admirals and been nervous, and do it by myself. Tapping works.

—Carmelo Cruz Diaz
Seven-year Army veteran

* * *

 ## "I Don't Need All These Medications I'm Taking"

I'm a combat vet. Viet Nam, 1966-1967. At age 18, I was scared like all the rest of us were. They handed me a weapon, and introduced me to what they called "the enemy." I didn't want to kill, but that's what I was trained to do.

I remember blood and guts everywhere, [but] to this day, I can't remember one member of my unit's name. From my lieutenant to my sergeant, not even my comrades.

I did my job. I protected my comrades as best I could. I was willing to give my life because our government said so. I did what I was told. But to this day, I think about the people I murdered. I will never forget them.

[After I returned], I worked 18 different jobs. I didn't understand why I couldn't get along with people—why I wanted to get away from them including my own relatives. They couldn't understand what was wrong with me. I didn't understand what was wrong with me.

I would get up in the middle of the night and just go out. My children would beg me not to leave—my wife would beg me not leave. I couldn't explain why. I never talked about it.

After all the conditions I dealt with, I've got 20 medications [for] depression, sleep, this and that.

I went to the VA. Next thing I know, they were talking about PTSD. Then I understood I had a problem. I found out through my Congressman and my Senator that the best PTSD programs in the country were in Palo Alto, Hawaii, New Mexico, Wyoming, Wisconsin. I bought a one-way ticket [to Hawaii] because I wasn't leaving until I [got] the help I needed.

I thought with the tap-tap stuff, "Whoa, this ain't gonna fly with the VA."

I tried it. It makes you focus memory on forgetting about what your experiences were. And it helps you cope when you see these events in your mind.

I have a son in Iraq on his fifth tour. That stresses me. I have a son in India. That stresses me. I have to keep up with current events in case something happens to my sons. I see events on TV. But the treatment I received—without medication—has made a big difference and a change in my life. I don't need all these medications I'm taking. And I'm here to testify to that.

I'm going to send a copy of [my TFT] evaluation to the Veterans Administration, to all 535 members of Congress, to the White House, and I'm going see what they do with it.

That's my story.

—Charles G. Hayward, Sr.
Combat veteran in Viet Nam

* * *

Whether a soldier returned from battle 40 years ago or 40 days ago, TFT works the same—"re-categorizing" the way the brain stores emotional information surrounding the trauma of war.

In this next compelling story, no job in the military could be as traumatic as burying the dead—a daily task filled with images, sounds, and smells that this serviceman will never forget.

" The Smell of War

The Gulf War was a short war and a war with few Allied casualties. And yet one young soldier, we'll call him "Gary," left a large part of himself back in the large flat desert to the North of Kuwait.

He wanted that part of himself back.

The war was officially over. The multitude of invading tanks and infantry had retreated and formed a long contiguous line stretching from the North of Kuwait and into Iraq. The tanks had been disabled, most burned by the Allied Forces beyond recognition. The bulldozers had plowed the Iraqi tanks into trenches, sometimes inadvertently burying live Iraqi soldiers, still entombed in their sandy graves, arms sticking up here and there from the sand.

Gary's job was to bury the dead. Cleanup duty.

The sight of charred Iraqi bodies and eyes still staring out from burned corpses haunted him. But even more, it was the smell of charred flesh he remembered most. It was a smell that wouldn't leave him.

It had been over a year and Gary was still paralyzed by the sights and especially the smells of war. He was not available to his wife. He was not available to his two small children. And work was not going well. Gary numbed the sights and smells with the bottle when possible, providing his only relief but causing even more problems in his life. It was the only form of relief he could find, despite some attempts at therapy.

Gary thought that the idea of tapping while he focused on the sights and smells frozen in his memory was a little crazy, but he was willing to try anything. As we tapped, Gary reported that the visual memories began to fade and seemed far away and lost their charge. The smells from the past that seemed to permeate his world in the present didn't go away as easily. But they, too, eventually disappeared with more TFT. Soon Gary was present to his family and doing well at work, no longer haunted by the sights and smells left behind in the desert.

He was finally home. "

—Suzanne M. Connolly, LCSW

We're committed to helping our military recover from the trauma of war. TFT can help. But another part of that work—through the ATFT Foundation—is to encourage timeshare owners to donate their unused timeshare weeks so returning soldiers can enjoy some much-needed rest, relaxation and trauma relief with their families.·

This next story illustrates why this program is so close to the hearts of people working with returning service members.

Those Innocent Objects at the Side of the Road

Recent warfare has featured the increasing use of IED's (Improvised Explosive Devices) that have caused many of the deaths and injuries to allied forces in Iraq and Afghanistan. An IED often looks benign as an object of little notice on the side of the road., but it is exploded by a terrorist with horrendous results as troops drive past it.

A client of mine had his vehicle blown up by an IED in Iraq.

"The attack caused serious harm to my men," he said.

He told me how, after two years at home, he still feels heightened anxiety as he drives roads and highways whenever he sees a box, a can or other seemingly innocuous object alongside the road. He almost begins to panic and gets sick to his stomach.

Upon hearing this, we immediately did a brief TFT trauma treatment. This helped, he said—but he didn't move all the way to zero on the SUD scale (*subjective units of distress*). I then used advanced TFT diagnostic procedures with him and added two additional tapping points to the standard sequence.

We then went for a drive to see if the TFT worked for him. He drove me around town, and on almost every block we would spot a box or something—including suspicious looking cars that ordinarily would spark his anxiety. He was frankly amazed and did not know what to make of the change he experienced as his IED anxiety did not present itself.

---

* For more information, please visit www.atftfoundation.org or www.timesharesforvets.com.

He said he can now relax while driving. He told me that he had driven hundreds of miles the week before to see Veterans Administration psychiatrists and doctors in different cities to "be evaluated but not treated."

Interestingly, two weeks before this TFT change in him, he had been treated for joint pain by Dr. Callahan and me, and mentioned that he did not need to take two of his three medications since then.

The trauma caused by IED's is a widespread problem which TFT can help resolve.

—*Herb Ayers, MA, LMHC*

* * *

It's no secret that people suffering from the trauma of hostile environments can benefit greatly from the results TFT provides.

But what about trauma that's closer to home?

Sadly, millions of men, women and children are traumatized at some point in their lives—causing ongoing physical ailments, addictions, and compulsive behaviors even decades later. Luckily, Thought Field Therapy gets to the root of these problems—alleviating the trauma itself so their lives can become more relaxed, fulfilling and productive.

In this story of violence close to home, one woman triumphs 20 years later over trauma and the related disorders it caused.

 Rising Above Painful Memories

More than 20 years ago, on a date with her 18-year-old boyfriend, "Barbara" was raped. At the time, she was just 13 years old.

In the years following the event, severe trauma, violent memories and a low self-image caused continuous suffering. By the time she had reached her mid-thirties, Barbara had problems with drugs and alcohol. She suffered severe bouts of depression with suicidal intent. And she exhibited a number of other symptoms that doctors had categorized as major depression, bipolar disorder, drug dependence, and borderline personality disorder. She had received treatment at a number of rehab facilities—both residential and outpatient—yet she wasn't well at all when I first took her on as a client.

When Barbara discussed the rape with me, she appeared to be "re-living" it to some extent. She cried deeply and expressed profound remorse—referring to herself in the most negative terms. I quickly interrupted this episode by having her instead describe the environment she saw, heard, smelled, and tangibly felt. After she calmed down, I told her that I was working with a technique—Thought Field Therapy—that might help to relieve the pain she felt each time she thought about this event.

She was willing to give it a try.

Within several minutes of treating her for psychological reversal· and tapping out the basic trauma sequence, Barbara no longer felt emotional pain while reviewing the memory.

What amazed me even more, however, was the fact that Barbara's beliefs about herself *and* the incident were simultaneously transformed. For example, I asked her what she thought about the event, and she replied in an almost casual tone that it was "just something that happened when I was a kid." I even pushed her a bit to test this result by asking with an accusing tone, "Don't you think that you were to blame? Don't you think it was your fault?"

Her response to me was an unshaken and softly stated, "No, I don't think I was to blame. I was just a kid."

This alteration was almost beyond belief! Just moments before, she had wept bitterly about what a no-good person she was, and now that self-hatred had completely disappeared!

Even a week after the treatment, she reported that she continued to not feel bothered about the rape. She told me that she tested this out several times over the week by thinking about the rape, and she did not feel any distress.

Years later, I saw Barbara and she continued to do well. Today, she is no longer dependent on drugs and alcohol and her

---

* Psychological reversal (or "PR") is a blockage or reversal of the energy flows in your body's energy pathways. It keeps all kinds of treatments from working as well as they should. PR can be easily eliminated by tapping midway on the outside edge of your hand prior to using other tapping sequences for your illness or disorder. TFT practitioners always test for PR prior to TFT treatment.

self-esteem appears to be on the rise. She went on to complete her Master's degree in social work, became licensed and entered practice as a psychotherapist. She also became involved administratively with the National Association of Social Workers, organizing their conferences.

—*Fred P. Gallo, PhD*

* * *

As brutal as rape and sexual abuse can be, other physical trauma can also set in motion a lifetime of debilitating disorders. When even simple tasks like cooking, talking on the phone, being in public places, working at a job and other normal activity become nearly impossible, TFT can help.

In this story of a young woman whose life blossoms following treatment, TFT brings her out of solitude and depression to achieve her lifelong dream.

 ## How I Rekindled the Song in My Heart

In 2000, I was diagnosed with post-traumatic stress disorder after a brutal physical attack. Because of my head injuries, I was unable to complete thoughts or make any sense of the world.

Debilitating depression followed, as even simple tasks like cooking became difficult. I suffered from severe anxiety and did not know how to engage in society. I became a relative hermit and put on a lot of weight.

All I could manage to do was eat, sleep and watch videos.

My depression grew and intense rage emerged as I ruminated day after day on the attack. Five years passed in this manner, until one day I was introduced to a local TFT practitioner who listened to my story and offered to give me a session of TFT.

I was skeptical. Yet after several treatments, I lost the depression and became more functional.

Soon, not only did my fear of people and being in public places disappear, but I began to rekindle my former career as a singer and songwriter—performing my songs at local venues. Previously, my memory had been so damaged due to head injuries that I had trouble remembering my songs. This improved using TFT.

I also became a TFT practitioner and continued to clear phobias, stress, confusion, love pain and rage as they emerged in my life. Chronic depression and anxiety became things of the past. And I realized with gratitude that I had started living my life again—but not only that, my life was better than it had been before the assault!

Within just a few years, I won a $1,000 first prize in a major local songwriter's quest and went on to record an album of my songs. I organized every detail of my own album launch which had been an unfulfilled dream for 30 years.

Today I have four different part-time businesses which I run myself—including a small TFT practice. I have many friends, hobbies and interests and am living the life I've always wanted to!

I am an active member of my community and the world at large, and feel that I have something to contribute. I have no doubt that I am capable of moving on to achieve even greater goals as my life unfolds.

This year, I will be 50 years old and have never been happier than I am right now. I believe that TFT has very significantly contributed to my healing process when very little else seemed to be working.

It is simple, fast and effective as a modality of therapy and easy to administer to myself and others when the need arises. I recommend it to anyone. I will continue to rely on its help, as it's an invaluable way to be free of all kinds of problems—whether mental, emotional or physical.

—Gabrielle Williamson

* * *

Physical harm from a traumatic event can leave lasting emotional wounds, regardless of the age, maturity, intelligence or judgment of the victim. In this story of childhood trauma, one

TFT practitioner recognizes that—for a 10-year-old girl—the aftereffects have become unbearable.

 ## Trauma When a School Prank Goes Awry

In one of my many professional capacities, I act as a volunteer mediator. This work is both interesting and rewarding to me. The program for which I mediate involves first- and second-time juvenile offenders—ages 7 to 17. Mediation brings the victim and offender together in a non-court setting. The process gives the victim the opportunity to confront the offender with the financial, emotional, physical, and other effects that resulted from his or her offense.

The result of the process, when successful, is that the victim receives some form of restitution which the victim and offender agree to. The benefits are that the offender can reframe their priorities and choose a different life path. My work as the mediator is to guide the parties toward a mutual agreement— and to structure the process so that all parties are respected, honest, and focused on the issues at hand.

A few weeks back, I took part in such a mediation in South Los Angeles. The victim was a 10-year old African American girl, who we will call "Felicity." The offender was an 11-year-old African American boy, who we will call "Michael." Parents of both young people were also present. Both were students in the same class at school at the time of the incident.

That day, Michael tried to play a practical joke on Felicity while she was away from her seat delivering papers to the school office. Michael put a pencil in her seat, much as children of old used to put gum or tacks on the seats of other youngsters. This time, however, the results were far different. Felicity did not see the pencil, and sat on it. Unfortunately, the pencil became impaled in her buttock area.

With a combination of pain, guilt, and embarrassment, Felicity went to the teacher to tell what had happened. The teacher did not see evidence of the wound at first, which only brought more unwanted attention to the girl. She finally convinced the teacher to let her go see the nurse. The nurse could (or would) do nothing substantial for her.

Finally, Felicity's parents were called. Her father had to come to get her and transport her to the hospital, where surgery was done to remove the pencil.

Michael was suspended from school and later banned from the campus as a result of this incident. He was also arrested. Being a first-time offender, he qualified for our mediation program, so the probation officer referred the case to me.

During mediation, Felicity and Michael wept as they described the incident and its aftereffects. Michael had written Felicity a letter of apology, which he gave to Felicity at the mediation. He tearfully said that he was sorry for what he had done, and that he had not intended to hurt her. The mediation reached a conclusion that satisfied all parties; financial compensation and community service were included in the agreement.

Yet as my co-mediator and I were completing the paperwork, it became evident that the traumatic episode itself was not over.

Felicity's mother mentioned that her daughter was suffering a number of challenges as a result of this tragic event. She experienced flashbacks when approaching her seat at school fearing that she would sit on a pencil again. She had been unable to sleep well during the weeks following the event. And her grades were going down. We also learned that Michael had been suffering nightmares related to his role in this event.

I had not immediately thought of applying TFT to this situation because I was focused on the mediation process. However, as Michael and his family left, Felicity's mother asked where she might get some assistance for her daughter.

I suggested that I might be able to help.

I told the parents that I was trained in a therapy that had proven very effective with traumas such as this, and that if they wished, I would be glad to assist them free of charge.

A week later, I met with Felicity, her parents, and my co-mediator, who is also a social worker. He was intrigued by my description of relieving trauma by "tapping." I began with the issue of the pain from being impaled by the pencil, and using the pain algorithm, reduced her Subjective Units of Distress (SUD) from 10 to 1. I then used the anxiety algorithm to address the anxiety over sitting in her seat at school, also reducing the SUD from 10 to 1.

I tested for other issues, and found none present. Felicity was so relieved that she was giggling, laughing—in short, she was transformed. Her parents were thrilled, and my good friend the co-mediator was equally impressed.

I've also been in contact with Michael's parents, and unfortunately, his nightmares continue. I made the same offer to Michael and am scheduling a date soon to work on overcoming his post-traumatic distress.

—*Lionel Mandy*

* * *

Many victims put their lives back together after severe physical injury—only to suffer ongoing physical problems related to their injury. These lasting injuries are often explained away in medical terms, with the patient never considering that a psychological or emotional aftereffect is at work.

TFT can often help correct lasting physical damage *that may not be physically caused after all.*

The Gift of Smell

During one snowy January five years ago, I went sledding down my street. As I picked up speed, I didn't realize that part way down the steep hill, the snow had turned to ice. I was unable to steer or stop, and slid head first into the bumper of a parked mini-van.

I suffered such a critical head injury that I barely made it to the hospital alive. If it had taken the ambulance 20 minutes longer, it would have been too late.

I was put into a medical coma for 10 days and still don't remember the two-month period after the accident. With great medical care, support from my family, and post-hospital rehabilitation, I finally returned to full-time work after 8 months.

While in every other respect I was nearly fully recovered, I had lost 100% of my sense of smell. My doctors told me that the loss of smell is not an unusual occurrence after the type of brain injury I suffered. Unfortunately, they also told me I would never recover this ability.

For five years, they were correct.

Then a chance email reached me about a TFT teleseminar being given by Dr. Roger Callahan. During the teleseminar, he gave me a customized Thought Field Therapy tapping sequence designed to help me regain my sense of smell.

I used the algorithm about 20 times a day for 40 consecutive days, and after the 30th day, I was startled and pleasantly surprised to notice the air suddenly seemed different as I walked down the indoor hallway near the cafeteria in my building. It took me a minute to realize I was actually smelling something again!

After five years, I had almost forgotten what it was like.

In the days since then, I have had other instances of smelling things. My sense of smell is not yet back to 100%, but I am thrilled to *have actually experienced a healing* that doctors told me could never happen.

TFT has made this possible.

Dr. Callahan originally explained I would need to use the tapping sequence 15+ times a day for many weeks. It only takes a minute to do, and it can been done throughout the day. I gladly and enthusiastically continue applying TFT to further regain my sense of smell. This is much better than five years of thinking I would never smell again!

Plus, I now use different TFT algorithms to alleviate other challenges such as worry and anxiety.

—*David Burns*

* * *

Thousands of people every year sustain brain injury from accidents, strokes, and other types of health related illnesses. Head Trauma can be very debilitating and frustrating for the victim as they experience changes to their daily routine and relationships. Each phase of their recovery comes with a new set of emotions and challenges to deal with as they rebuild their life.

Many of them have relapses in the healing process because of short term memory challenges. They may have to completely relearn daily tasks that we take for granted like walking, eating, dressing, and even just communicating.

In this next story from an advanced TFT practitioner, four different clients with previous traumatic brain injury become more relaxed and less anxious with just one session.

In Session Two, they report their memory and concentration has improved. By the third session of TFT—after eliminating dietary toxins and other household toxins they were sensitive to (which helped reduce depression)—most of them noticed a remarkable difference in being able to retain information and concentrate for longer spans of time.

Read what their own TFT practitioner has to say about their recovery process.

 ## Recovering from Traumatic Brain Injury

Sally was a high school math and science teacher and thoroughly loved her job working with teenagers. In the blink of an eye, however, her life changed forever as a bookshelf of textbooks fell on her head, crushing the vertebrae in her neck.

"There was only so much the doctors could do to repair the bones and nerve damage," she told me.

Eventually put on permanent disability, she suffered migraines, severe pain in her neck and shoulders, and memory loss. Concentration was difficult—causing major frustration as she failed at even ordinary tasks. Because Sally was divorced, she had to rely on other family members for her care. Finances were slim which added even more stress. Depressed and anxious, she finally turned to TFT.

Another client, Gary, had suffered Traumatic Brain Injury (TBI) in a motorcycle accident near his home in Florida. I never met him in person, but instead worked with him over the phone.

He was wearing his helmet when he slammed into a tree to avoid hitting a car that pulled out in front of him, but the impact alone was enough to break his neck and cause major bruising to the brain. Not only that, but some 30 other bones were broken.

No one expected Gary to live.

He remained in the hospital for six months fighting just to stay alive. Reconstructive surgery followed to rebuild the shattered bones in his face.

Miraculously, after 10 years, he was able to walk with a cane and had learned to use a computer which is his key to communication. He was in quite a bit of pain daily—and his memory was very limited. His biggest challenge was doing tasks that required multiple steps. As he succumbed to depression and anxiety, drinking became a way to self-medicate which added to the complexity of working with him.

In client case study #3, my father Dale suffered massive brain damage when—during emergency heart-bypass surgery—he was given iodine which caused a violent allergic reaction, shock and swelling of the brain. Almost every drug his doctors gave him during his "recovery" caused further reactions and symptoms. His skin became sensitive, his memory sketchy, and he had such shortness of breath, he could hardly walk from the house to the car. For three years, he suffered the aftereffects of trauma, becoming sensitive to nearly every kind of food including wheat, soy, corn and dairy.

A fourth client, Jeff, had suffered a head injury nine years earlier while in college. He was attacked one night and brutally beaten with a pipe wrench. As a result, he suffered from short term memory loss, sleeping issues, challenges with concentration, and fear and anxiety around studying and test taking.

As a writer for a magazine while studying for the bar exam, these symptoms would create anxiety as it was difficult for him to remember details and concentrate for long periods of time.

Jeff's diet also had to change. Many types of alcohol, caffeine and scented products were sensitivities for him. Doctors prescribed various beta blockers and ADD-type drugs to help with concentration and anxiety—yet these medications caused fatigue and other side-effects which were just as intolerable.

All four of these clients improved with TFT.

The first thing I worked on with them was to clear the trauma around their head injury. I used the TFT trauma tapping sequence which usually brought their SUD—*subjective units of distress*—down 2 or 4 points on the scale of 0 to 10.

After that, I taught them basic sequences to work on individual emotions they were experiencing such as anger, frustration, depression and pain, anxiety and embarrassment. By teaching individual tapping sequences, they had tools to use outside of our sessions as the emotions appeared—and before they could get out of hand and impede physical progress.

After just one session, all four of these clients felt more relaxed and less anxious. After session two, they reported their memory and concentration was getting better. By session three, most of them were noticing a remarkable difference in being able to retain information and concentrate for longer periods of time.

Pain management was also much better.

Interestingly, in all four cases, we had to identify individual toxins that were preventing a reduction of symptoms when tapping. All four clients were sensitive to their laundry detergent; some were sensitive to wheat, sugar, corn and dairy; and still others were sensitive to personal care products and other foods or beverages. I realized by working with them that their body's immune system was weakened after their injuries—so they were more sensitive to items they tolerated before their trauma.

After clearing these toxins with the TFT 7-Second Toxin Treatment, we were able to proceed with the tapping sequences. Eliminating toxins from their environment also helped remove symptoms of anxiety and depression.

Thought Field Therapy has truly been instrumental in the healing process for all four clients.

—*Christina Mayhew*

* * *

What's interesting about the four clients with brain injuries is that the trauma caused not only massive physical harm—but also trauma to the mind when secondary disorders like depression, anxiety, short-term memory loss and rage took hold in their lives.

In this next story about a teenage boy with Downs Syndrome and Autism—we discover that even those with a previously existing *genetic brain injury* can benefit from trauma relief.

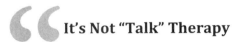 It's Not "Talk" Therapy

As the 17-year-old boy flopped into a chair in my office, I knew right away TFT was the right therapy to help him. A victim of violence by his day-program worker, he is an African-American boy, quiet, very engaging and cute!

He was also born with Downs Syndrome and Autism.

He lives with both of his parents and a younger sister in Los Angeles. To communicate, he uses sign language and a communication board to spell out, letter by letter, any words he wants to say—as his verbal output does not always match what he intends to say. He also uses sign language (finger spelling) and some American Sign Language.

Because of the moderate level of mental retardation that he has, I knew "typical" talk therapy would not work to help him recover from his trauma. In fact, talk therapy is never used in my practice with individuals with cognitive impairments to begin with. But I have found that TFT can have a quick and significant effect.

At our second session I introduced TFT in action, having "prepared" the parents for the unusual, yet non-verbal, approach I planned. This teenager needed quite a bit of modeling, assistance from his father, and encouragement to participate in the tapping, but he definitely did not want to be the only person in the room not tapping!

I asked the father to first do the tapping completely while focusing on the trauma, and then "pass" the treatment to the boy by touching him after the first treatment.

After just one sequence, the teen was able to do it on his own.

After the 3rd tapping treatment—actually, just before ending the final sequence—he began yawning, then giggling. I knew then that he was feeling better.

Just to check his progress in releasing the trauma, I asked him to think again about the traumatic event, and he shook his head and giggled. He was done.

At the conclusion of the session, as I was escorting them all back to the exit, he turned, firmly grabbed and shook my hand, and said, "Good job!"

His parents looked at me, amazed! He had never done that before! Although they often tell him, "good job" when he has done something well, they had never seen him use this term, especially with appropriateness of the comment!

Since that time, whenever we are in session and he feels he needs help, he begins tapping on the eyebrow point, and away we go. When he starts to yawn, I know we are done.

He has not asked to tell me what is bothering him, first of all because I do not need to know—and secondly, because using words in this way was difficult and tedious for him.

His parents were excited about his improvement, and have learned much about TFT and its application for their own trauma and anger around his traumatic event. Of course, I was completely thrilled with the effect of TFT, and with the joyousness of his spirit.

—*Nora J. Baladerian, PhD*

* * *

As the story above shows, trauma relief with TFT is fast, non-invasive and simple—even for those with limited speech, diminished reasoning abilities or lack of maturity.

While this teenage boy was lucky enough to receive help quickly for his trauma, others live for years with the aftereffects of the event. They may try dozens of different therapeutic approaches to erase the memories, pain and negative effect on their lives.

In this next story about a woman who at first refused to try TFT, a single tapping sequence brings her immediate relief from decades of flashbacks, suicidal tendency and seclusion following a childhood filled with trauma.

 ## Like Acupuncture for the Mind

Having regressed to my life as a 4-year-old—crouched, screaming and fighting off imaginary blows—I was hospitalized for the second time in 10 years. The first time, I had been released after four days as the safety of the hospital had brought me out of *abreaction* (the reliving of events as if happening at the present moment), and my functions returned to normal. This second time though, the flood gates opened and spilled over my years of insistent denial. The physical, sexual and psychological traumas of childhood poured forth.

Many devoted healthcare professionals worked with me over the next 20 years. Blessed breakthroughs did come in the way of integrating the past with the present and changes in the way I acted out that pathology. However, after trying every new therapy for PTSD that came along—the night terrors, flashbacks and regressions continued.

After retiring to Sedona Arizona, and though living a wonderfully rewarding lifestyle, I still suffered from PTSD. Just seeing something familiarly violent on a television show might trigger days of dissociation, self mutilation (the act of inflicting pain on self by cutting) and regressions.

Having learned over the years that PTSD symptoms are never completely eliminated, I dealt with these episodes as they came by staying recluse for periods of time. After one recurrent triggering event left me suicidal, I again sought help from the mental health community.

I was introduced to a therapist who, after listening to my story, asked if I would be willing to try an unconventional therapy that involved tapping on points of the body while recalling the trauma. I politely told her, "NO!"

Spiritually devoted and as open a person as I am, I was not going to spend time and money on some 'Sedona Woo-Woo' technique.

I suggested we stick with regular therapy.

Two sessions later, she mentioned she would be out of town for the next month (doing her woo-woo in some other country). She asked if we could try one small bit of Thought Field Therapy—a sort of acupuncture for the mind. I felt silly tapping, humming and counting—then humming again as she instructed. But I did so.

To my shock, I immediately felt relief.

My whole body dropped the stress and distress.

She asked how I felt. Almost in tears, I said that I felt the first relief I had known in six weeks. Although overwhelmed with gratitude, I said that this was surely a placebo response and that I would withhold any applause till tomorrow.

Six years later, I am still free of being triggered and re-triggered over this childhood trauma. One by one, each individual incident was tapped away. I now remember these past events but am free of emotional reaction to them. No more days of dissociation and panic. When periodic new memories do arise, I tap them away. Although I thought TFT was too too good to be true, I now know that it embodies many truths.

Family and friends are astounded by the change in me, and say things like, "Remember how you were for days on end?" or "I used to be worried when we were out together that something would trigger you."

I now have taken the Thought Field Therapy training so I can help others when possible. I also contribute financially and with personal efforts to promote TFT's work in war-torn and disaster areas around the globe. I am all too aware that victims of such atrocities cannot begin to help themselves, no matter how much money is poured into assistance, until the traumas are relieved and the people can function.

I now have a vision. I see a world where the cycle of abuse, passed from one person to another, reverses into a cycle of healing as people pass on the gift of TFT. I imagine the prison population dwindling, the traumatized homeless thriving, and men and women coming home from war able to function.

The implications of the good TFT can bring to the world are endless. It is my hope that all who have experienced or witnessed the effectiveness of TFT will work toward and see a day when it is a mainstream treatment. I liken it to acupuncture which, once scoffed at as snake oil, is now giving relief from physical pain to so many—and it is so proven that it is now accepted and paid for by insurance companies and Medicare.

Thank you TFT.

—Michelle (Miki) Butterworth

* * *

What surprises most PTSD sufferers is the sheer speed with which they find relief following a TFT treatment—and quite often *during treatment.* Not only that, but TFT has lasting effects that endure—even under the daily stress of violent images on television, sounds that can trigger a flashback, emotions that emerge at inconvenient times, and other forms of daily suffering.

In this harrowing story, one woman regains control of her life and emotions through TFT—and at the time of this writing, was still enjoying peace and relief four years after her treatment.

Nothing Worked Until I Discovered TFT

I was terrified of men and hadn't dated for nearly 16 years. When I was 15 years old, I was kidnapped and raped by an acquaintance.

I felt guilty, ashamed, and frightened yet somehow responsible.

I had been walking home from school and it was a long walk. He drove up, smiling, and offered me a ride. I knew I shouldn't have, but I got into his car and the nightmare began. I remember the kidnapping, but had repressed the rape ordeal.

Since then I've tried many ways to resolve this issue—therapy, journal writing, Emotional Freedom Technology, but nothing worked. I even became a rape counselor, and while it helped—the trauma remained.

Then, a good friend told me about a TFT seminar that was being taught locally. At that point, I was ready to try anything that might work. Our group was small and was comprised solely of women—so I felt safe.

The TFT treatments were new to me and at first, I was thoroughly confused. However, as we practiced on each other, I found that others experienced real relief immediately. I hoped that I could, as well.

When the seminar leader asked for volunteers, I was one of the first to raise my hand. I didn't know what to expect, but I was open to the experience. I didn't care that others would be staring at me, because I so wanted to be free of my trauma.

My SUD level—or *subjective units of distress*—was a "9" out of "10." As I continued to tap, I focused on the event all those years ago—and emotions came over me like rolling waves. Tears rolled down my cheeks as I saw that tawdry room, felt the butcher knife at my throat, and breathed the stench of his unclean body atop mine.

I felt a distance between me and what I saw in my mind, so I was never frightened. As my SUD number dropped, I saw myself on my knees—and realized this was how my decade-long knee pain had begun. By now, I was angry—and then I saw his face.

In all of the years since the rape, I had buried this trauma—and his face—yet here he was. But now, because of the TFT treatment, *I was in control.*

Using a few profane words, I told him to get up and leave and never come back. He did.

My treatment was over.

Astonishingly, my knee pain was gone. MY SUD was now a "0." And I was beaming in front of the seminar group. I felt triumph, peace and joy. And while I still have the memory, it is distant as if it happened to someone else. That was four years ago, yet the trauma still remains a thing of the past. I no longer fear men. In fact, I have a number of men in my life who are wonderful friends. And I'm dating again. The treatment lasted just 45 minutes, yet I experienced an extraordinary and lasting miracle due to TFT.

—*Roxane Williams*

* * *

What could have been a lifetime of pain and suffering for Roxane was instead erased by the restorative effects of TFT. Even when nothing else worked for her, Thought Field Therapy took away the painful emotions she experienced whenever the memory of the trauma surfaced.

Her recovery hints at the difference between TFT and traditional therapy which tries to deal with the *memory* of the event. In our experience, it's so much easier to simply take away the emotional and mental pain associated with the memory. While the memories of the traumatic event remain with the victim, after TFT the victim will no longer respond to it in a painful, emotional way.

As Roxane says, "While I still have the memory, it is distant, as if it happened to someone else." Therein lies the unique benefit of Thought Field Therapy—its ability to eliminate trauma's hold on the victim.

But how does TFT work for people who have experienced trauma, yet do not have any memories of trauma—nor are they even aware that disturbing aftereffects exist? Read this next story about an elderly woman who was relieved of delusional behavior with the help of TFT following a traumatic surgery.

 The Day Time Became Broken

In early December, I received a referral from a General Practitioner concerning an elderly lady patient, "Marie," whom he described as having an Obsessive Compulsive Disorder (OCD). It arose almost immediately following her coronary bypass surgery some two to three years earlier. The problem seemed to revolve around Marie's obsessive belief that her grown-up and independent daughters (aged 40 and 28) were still young children, Marie referring to them as her "little ones"—and that the elderly gentleman living with her (Mike, her husband) was her eldest son (aged 41). She also had difficulty in recognizing her grandchildren, always asking who they were when they visited.

At mealtimes she would lay the table for five and become very anxious when neither her "little ones" nor her husband had returned home at the expected time. When Mike attempted to explain the reality of the situation to Marie, she would become angry and aggressive, refusing to believe the version of events she was being given.

Psychiatric intervention and cognitive therapy had failed to resolve the problem, and it was thought that a lack of oxygen to the cerebral cortex—as a consequence of the earlier surgery— was to blame. Alzheimer's disease was tentatively put forward as a diagnosis, but rejected. Finally, an MRI scan showed slight deterioration of the brain although within the bounds of normal aging.

When I visited Marie and her husband Mike in their own home to familiarize myself with the situation, it rapidly became clear that she did not have a classical OCD but what I might call a "time distortion delusion." It appeared that time for Marie had slipped back 25 years, but only in relation to her perception of her immediate family. Current events and situations were clear to her, but when asked about her "little ones," she referred to her grown-up daughters as school-age girls. In addition, when asked about her husband, she thought that he was at work and that her son was visiting (actually 300 miles away, working in London).

I then explained to Marie that I wanted to diagnose and treat her, and that she should think about her problem as clearly as possible. Unfortunately, Marie vigorously denied she had a problem and therefore could not possibly think about it. In a moment of inspiration, I asked Marie to "think about the little ones at school."

I first deduced that the TFT tapping sequence for post-traumatic stress disorder (PTSD) was appropriate. This came as no surprise, since the triggering event for Marie's problem had been her traumatic bypass surgery. I continued my diagnostic process and found another tapping sequence and mini psychological reversal for Marie. After completing this tapping, Marie no longer showed distress about her "little ones" nor about her husband, who was sitting nearby.

Just to be sure, I measured the results by questioning Marie.

I asked her about her "little ones at school." At once, she told me about her granddaughters and how she adored them. When I asked who the elderly gentleman sitting in the room was, she replied, "My husband."

To test her further, I became much more confrontational and accused Marie of "neglecting her own children who were waiting for her to collect them from school." She then apologized for contradicting me, but pointed out that they could not be at school as they all had responsible jobs.

"Who are your little ones, then?" I asked.

"My grandchildren," she answered readily.

I continued this assertive style of questioning but no trace of the time-distortion illusion could be reactivated. Mike then asked to question Marie himself and he was delighted to witness the complete resolution of Marie's problem. Of equal note was the fact that his wife's aggressive response to being corrected or questioned had also disappeared, Marie apologized if she had ever misled anyone, but she was sure she hadn't. Mike commented most happily on his wife's "calmness."

Just to complete the treatment, I tested Marie for various toxins—and discovered a sensitivity to coffee, sugar and saccharin. I advised her to avoid contact with those items, with her husband promising to monitor her diet.

Marie is now almost completely free of her problem, with only occasional minor relapses occurring which respond immediately to re-treatment.

In discussing the case with Dr. Roger Callahan, we agreed that the triggering event for the problem was probably toxic exposure—in this case, the anesthetic gas used during Marie's bypass surgery. Such exposure also increases sensitivity to other toxins which may have previously been no problem for Marie.

Such delusions can easily occur following major surgery, as can the onset of anxiety. The fact that TFT was very successful in this case points towards a very different explanation than the medically accepted "cortical degeneration" that is usually given as a cause for dementia-like symptoms.

—Ian Graham

Tapping Away Trauma and Its Aftermath

You'll find videos that step you through the complete tapping sequences for complex traumas at our website:

www.rogercallahan.com/pathways

Chapter Three:
Erasing the Stress Caused by Toxins

While situations such as domestic violence, poverty, substance abuse and terminal illness are a frequent cause of ongoing stress, only a modest percentage of the population will experience such stressors in their lifetime.

For the rest of us, however, there are toxins—a much more pervasive cause of stress that we're repeatedly exposed to every day, in the foods we eat, the clothes we wear, the products we use and the environment we live in. Unlike poisonous chemicals or caustic substances, toxins—as we define them—are anything to which your own unique body reacts negatively. While your neighbor might be sensitive to coffee, you may find a particular brand of laundry detergent to be toxic. While others may never react badly to dairy, wheat, eggs or soy—your body may react strongly to these common food toxins in your diet.

Of course, these reactions may not be violent enough to cause alarm. But they still cause stress and imbalances to the body because they upset the body's energy systems—those energy pathways that regulate all function, emotion, chemical processes, and response to disease.

In actuality, the body usually responds in *much less noticeable* ways such as by causing depression, heightening our anxiety and phobias, making us hyperactive, retaining fluids and building up internal mucus, creating a skin disorder, fostering a personality disorder or affecting the memory. Unfortunately, these disorders are often explained as being the result of something else entirely. And while most medical practitioners will simply treat the symptoms of these disorders, those of us in the healing profession who look constantly *at underlying causes* will usually identify specific toxins as the culprit.

When you ingest or are exposed to what we call an Individual Energy Toxin—even if it's considered organic or "healthy" food— it disrupts *your* body's finely tuned energy pathways. This impact to your underlying, fundamental energy system further creates a change at the next level up...the chemical level, impacting the body's electrical, hormonal, circulatory, nervous, digestive and other systems.

The end result of this chain-reaction is that your body experiences repeated stress that is ultimately just as damaging as brutality, an accident, a vicious crime or other violent event.

In the following stories from TFT practitioners, we begin to see toxins at work—not only causing stress, but also preventing long-term relief after treatment. Take a look.

Toxins, Triumph and the Cigarette Switch

More and more, I see new clients who are suffering the negative effect of toxins on their body and mind. Either they've failed to get relief from other treatment options due to toxins—or they've achieved 100% relief with TFT, only to see their disorders return.

I remember meeting one client who was suffering from severe panic attacks, generalized anxiety and an obsessive compulsive disorder in which he repeatedly "flashbacked" to a time in his life when he contemplated committing a very severe crime—though he did not follow through on his plan.

To rid himself of this habitual flashback—plus his anxiety and panic attacks—he had tried different kinds of therapy to no avail. Some treatments, such as hypnosis, neurolinguistic programming and TFT with other practitioners, had helped somewhat, but shortly after leaving each session, his anxiety and flashbacks returned.

Now a man of 34, he was sometimes suicidal and permanently anxious—repeatedly experiencing the obsessive flashbacks. I used TFT to rid him of his OCD—yet after leaving our session, his symptoms returned less than 10 minutes later.

Guessing that toxins might be affecting this man, I called Dr. Callahan who confirmed that smoking might be the culprit. When I asked the client if he smoked, he readily answered, "Yes."

I instructed him not to smoke the day of our next session, and in addition, I went through a checklist of other toxins to identify substances, foods or products that might be reversing the gains he experienced in treatment.

Unfortunately, nothing would shift these reversals.

Then, during our next session, I noticed the client's cigarette pack in his shirt pocket. I promptly took them out of the room—and immediately his symptoms disappeared.

Through a twist of fate, however, someone walked down the hall of the clinic as my client and I were in session. When they saw the cigarette pack on the floor outside our door—they innocently brought the cigarettes back into the room, placing them on the table next to my client without his noticing.

Immediately, the OCD symptoms returned. I again took the cigarettes out of the room, and when I returned seconds later, the client said his SUD—*subjective units of distress*—had "mysteriously" dropped again. Then I told him what had just happened.

Not only was he surprised, he expressed that he was initially skeptical about the toxin effect. At that point, he also realized then he had been wasting his time in conventional therapy for over six years with zero results. No other therapist had identified toxins as a factor.

While that client case study was certainly illuminating for me, it took one more "toxic" client for me to realize the full danger of toxins and their contribution to anxiety disorders.

A relation of mine had lived with a disabling fear of her car door opening whilst driving, and of becoming lost whilst driving. She reported a constant feeling of anxiety in the pit of her stomach (almost always a sure sign of toxins, unless there is an imminent danger in the person's life that causes constant anxiety). After treating her for fear of driving, I didn't see her again until two days later when she appeared at my office—sobbing hysterically. She said she had just had a panic attack in the parking lot of her local shopping center after becoming terrified that she would get lost in a newly opened parking section.

The first thing I noticed after she walked in was a very powerful smell of her husband's aftershave. I asked her husband to wait in the lounge, while I took her into the garden.

Immediately, she calmed down.

I brought her in and out of the living room to test my suspicion about the aftershave, and each time, her SUD would intensify to "8" or "9" whenever she neared her husband. It was then that I realized that a toxin was behind her anxiety problem. Today, her husband is careful not to wear aftershave near her. Interestingly, her doctor told her that an overly sensitive sense of smell is a possible indicator of liver toxicity; she was recently diagnosed with liver problems.

Dr. Callahan's work identifying toxins' traumatic effect on the body and mind is, to me, some of the most underestimated medical information available today. So many unnecessary illnesses are caused by toxins. In fact, I have personally witnessed cancer recovery in three different people by identifying foods that are toxic to them individually—and seeing those patients eliminate the toxins from their diet.

In an example of household products that can be toxic to an individual, a client of mine had suffered from severe depression for three years after having prostate surgery and also losing his business. He had been in conventional therapy for those three years, and unfortunately had many times contemplated suicide. TFT was his last resort. After seven different sessions with him—nothing worked. Then a fellow TFT practitioner advised me to have the client change his brand of laundry detergent. Within a week, I received a call from the client saying he was fine and experiencing no more depression.

"Suddenly," he said, "it was just gone."

I asked him what had changed—whether he had started a new business, perhaps.

"Nothing different," he said.

I asked him whether he had changed his laundry detergent. Since his wife does the laundry, he asked her. She had bought a new brand of laundry detergent four days after our last session. The day the old detergent was removed from his home, his depression simply disappeared.

Three years later, he is still symptom-free and tells everyone he knows to try TFT.

—*Robert Grant*

*   *   *

If you suspect that toxins are the culprit behind your anxiety, phobias or post-traumatic stress, realize that identifying—then ridding yourself of—these harmful foods or products could prevent common illnesses, and even help prevent life-threatening diseases and debilitating disorders.

If you believe you have recently ingested something that is personally toxic to you, the "7-Second Toxin Treatment" can reverse the effect immediately.

While it is *not* a remedy for ingesting poisons, overdosing on prescription medications or being exposed to harmful chemicals or radioactive materials·, the 7-Second tapping sequence can address everyday "toxins" as we define them—foods, household cleaners, personal-care products, gasoline, dry cleaning solutions, even some fabrics used in clothing, all of which can affect our own body's unique chemistry.

Take a look now at how the 7-Second Toxin Treatment instantly worked for one young woman who suffered an allergic reaction to shellfish.

 ## A Shocking Reaction in Rural Croatia

While dining on vacation in rural Croatia, my 21-year-old daughter took a bite of shellfish and immediately developed a severe allergic reaction—heading rapidly into anaphylactic shock. As she was getting worse by the second, I applied the "7-Second Toxin Treatment" and—to our enormous relief—the reaction subsided after a few breaths. With further tapping, she calmed down considerably.

Later, however, she reacted badly (although less severely) to all manner of foods, including her necessary supplements and medicines. Using TFT, it was possible to gradually desensitize

---

* While often effective at lessening the impact of harmful or caustic substances, the 7-Second Toxin Treatment is not a substitute for immediate medical care from a hospital emergency room or advice from a poison control center. For a poison emergency in the U.S., call 1-800-222-1222 to be routed to one of your state's poison control centers.

her body enough for her to resume taking her medication. Although not designed for medical emergencies, the "7-Second" treatment can be a lifesaver.

—*Dr. Phil Mollon*

* * *

While ideal for correcting toxic overload that has developed in our bodies over time, the TFT tapping sequence for toxins also works for both recently ingested toxins that cause a dramatic change in behavior. In our experience, there is no better example of toxin-induced behavioral changes than young children who occasionally eat something "bad for them."

In this heartwarming story of a 4-year-old who suddenly becomes unusually hyperactive and incoherent while at lunch with the family, the TFT sequence for toxins brings her back to normal. Interestingly, because of the youngster's age, the TFT practitioner uses the "surrogate technique" of treating the mother while the little girl sits on her lap.

 "This Chinese Food"

Isn't it always this way? When something as simple and effective as TFT comes along, often people discount it as "too good to be true." However, it never occurred to me when I first became a TFT practitioner that the most difficult people to persuade would actually be my own family!

How did I convince them?

After returning home from my Diagnostic training with Dr. Callahan, I was presented with a perfect opportunity. We met for lunch as a family one Sunday—my wife Ana and my two children, my parents, sister and brother-in-law. We decided to have "take-out" Chinese food, and ordered an array of dishes.

My daughter, Megan, is nearly 4 years old, and is usually very well behaved, courteous and well spoken for her age (thanks to my wife's hard work). Shortly after starting our lunch, my wife and I noticed a sudden and noticeable change in Megan's behavior. I was reminded of the documentary, "Five Allergic Children" by Doris Rapp—and made the assumption that the Chinese food must have contained MSG or that Megan may have reacted to the soy. Megan's behavior deteriorated rapidly. She became hyper-active. But more noticeably, her language became "squeaky" and incoherent.

Because of her age and hyper-activity, it would have been nearly impossible to tap out a toxin treatment directly on her. So we had her sit on my wife's lap as I tapped out the standard toxin treatment on my wife using the words "This Chinese Food." The procedure took less than two minutes and the results were astonishing.

"Megan looks like she just woke up from a dream," my sister said.

The toddler seemed disoriented for a minute, then calmly sat down next to her aunt and started talking normally. She remained quiet and well behaved. It was proof for those family members watching that TFT, the surrogate process, and the toxin treatment is extremely effective.

I now plan to present this information to schools in my area, knowing that parents everywhere can use this technique to help themselves and their children.

—D.J. Wolfhaardt

* * *

Of course, we've all known for some time that certain foods—such as peanuts, shellfish and MSG—can cause violent allergic reactions in some people. But it's only *now* becoming widely recognized in the mainstream medical community that seemingly harmless foods can still be dangerous—even when they do not cause a severe reaction.

How?

When you ingest a food that is toxic to your personal body chemistry, your body—among other reactions—will store this toxin within your fatty tissue to keep it away from vital organs until the body has time to process and excrete the toxin days or even weeks later. The fat cells will retain water to dilute and "suspend" the toxin during this waiting period.

Some experts say that fat cells can expand up to 1,000 times their normal size as they retain this water. And with everyday toxins like wheat, dairy foods, eggs, soy, partially hydrogenated oil and other additives in abundance in our foods, it's no wonder that people have grown more obese in our modern society.

Without a doubt, toxins not only cause obesity—toxins cause trauma of the body and mind. In this next success story, a simple change in diet produced a tremendous change in appearance and emotional health for a World War II survivor.

 ## Shedding the Toxins, Losing the Weight

One of my clients spent her early childhood in displaced persons camps around Western Europe after World War II. Her family seldom had enough to eat, and she rarely had any meat. During her adult life, she gradually gained weight which she could not lose. She tried various diets and weight-loss plans, yet she simply could not lose the excess weight.

Initially, she approached me for counseling because of painful memories around her childhood experiences of being homeless. I used the trauma treatment with her and that was released immediately. After that, she wanted to focus on her weight.

I tested her and found her to be toxic for wheat and wheat products. She had had no previous indication of wheat causing a problem, but was willing to eliminate it from her diet. She became very creative about substituting for wheat in her baking and store purchases.

In less than a week, she noticed measurable weight loss! This was the first time she had ever lost weight on a regular basis. Since then, she's maintained her ideal weight, requiring only that she avoid wheat in her diet.

—Caroline A. Loose, PhD

* * *

No toxin is more tragic than the ones that cause a childhood disorder. Suddenly, a young life is robbed of the future of promise we envision for them.

But TFT can help, as we'll see in this next story about twin boys who were eventually removed from the Autistic Disorder Spectrum after TFT treatments and a toxin-free environment and diet.

 ## "We Began to Have No Hope for Recovery"

Our twin sons were placed on the Autism Disorder Spectrum when they were 18 months old. They showed signs of major delay and had yet to walk or talk. While they were extremely vocal, they had no language and they lacked common communication skills like pointing and clapping. After very slow and gradual progression, they began walking on their own at 20 months—but by 26 months they still had no language, even though they were in private speech therapy.

We turned to Norma Gairdner, who began treating my sons with Thought Field Therapy for various traumas. Additionally, she identified toxins and sensitivities to things the boys were regularly consuming or being exposed to, such as scented laundry products and air fresheners. After a session of TFT, the boys' general behavior and temperament seemed to change within that hour.

With a schedule of homeopathic remedies, elimination of various foods and chemicals, and lots of TFT (most often by phone), their language became recognizable and a gush of new words began to come from them daily.

Not only have the TFT treatments opened up the huge dam that was blocking the boys' development, but her unyielding dedication and relentless research into supportive and corrective supplements, cutting edge literature and progressive websites—to aid in further discovering a curative treatment—has been irrevocably and ultimately appreciated.

We had felt that our twins' "sentence" was for life, and looking around at the limited resources that western medicine recognizes, we began to have no hope for recovery.

Today, the boys are 3½ years old. They are walking, and talking (*all* the time), and both boys are extremely social and loving to everyone around them.

Better still, they have been officially removed from the Autistic Spectrum and began Kindergarten together in September.

—*as written to Norma Gairdner, HD
by the boys' mother*

Tapping Away the Stress Caused by Toxins

You'll find videos that step you through the complete tapping sequence for toxin relief at our website:

www.rogercallahan.com/pathways

Chapter Four:
Releasing Emotional Trauma: Anger, Guilt, Love Pain, Rejection & Grief

Trauma isn't limited to physical injury. Sometimes the trauma is emotional—a damage to the mind and spirit stemming from a sudden single incident or from a lengthier episode where the victim is exposed repeatedly to emotional abuse, violent episodes or ongoing unrelenting stress.

While some people survive such emotionally charged events without harm, others experience extreme emotional reactions such as uncontrollable crying, flashbacks, frightening memories, sleeplessness, nightmares and night terrors—even paranoia.

Victims may feel numb, disconnected, depressed, angry, guilty, sad, helpless or withdrawn from others.

But perhaps the most damaging symptom of emotional trauma is the illness or physical disorder that shows up years later—after you feel you've processed the hurt. You may never know why you are experiencing physical problems such as insomnia, weak vision, knee pain, fatigue, hypertension, or other aches and pains. In fact, your doctors may not be able to find any physical explanation at all, and simply attribute your illness to stress instead.

But a long-ago emotional trauma may be the cause.

Thought Field Therapy has been shown to be a powerful treatment for both recent and past emotional hurts that continue to damage the body or cause upset in our lives.

Of course, some emotional traumas are complex—with the victim showing signs of anger, rage, obsession or guilt along with their extreme emotions. TFT can calm these emotions and other symptoms by helping the mind correctly categorize the emotions related to the event. Many victims say after TFT that they still have the memories of the emotionally charged event, *but they no longer have negative feelings towards it.* The original disturbance—and their emotions—no longer have a hold over them.

But perhaps the most heartwarming application of TFT is when it helps a person who is grieving over the death of a loved one.

Grief can be an all-consuming emotion.

In fact, many grief counselors say it takes a year or more to "process" the feelings of grief related to losing someone or something you loved. And while many cultures around the world have historically formed elaborate traditions around this lengthy mourning period, we would like to offer a different viewpoint.

It isn't necessary to suffer such anguish.

Instead, imagine being able to put aside the emotional ravages of grief—the despair, depression, and melancholy—and simply recall the happy memories, love and compassion you had for that person.

Conventional therapy for grief often asks you to "feel the pain" and to embrace the loss. But how much more appropriate is it to honor your loved one by focusing on the happier times with them instead?

TFT makes this possible.

And the relief often occurs within minutes.

Whether you've ever experienced grief or an emotional trauma—or may have done so in the past without knowing it—you'll read about a solution in the stories that follow. In the first story, one TFT practitioner reveals how he treats "love pain"—the emotional suffering that occurs after the break-up of a romantic relationship.

 ## How Do You Mend a Broken Heart?

One of the most common forms of trauma is "love pain," a condition that's often made light of in the media, but which can bring on severe mental suffering that's often greater than bereavement. When a relationship ends, it leaves one feeling sad, angry, lost, abandoned, and often jealous, helpless and depressed.

In fact, every year, hundreds of people who are hurting commit suicide due to untreated love pain—with more men ending their lives than women.

I've treated a large number of cases of love pain using TFT, and in most cases, the tapping sequence for complex trauma—or complex trauma with anger and guilt—proves to be sufficient to relieve the symptoms within minutes.

Sometimes, however, the grief over a broken relationship causes other symptoms that begin to dominate a person's life. Recently, I treated a 39-year-old professional man who had suffered severe emotional distress since the break-up of a long-term romantic relationship six months earlier. As the months passed, he realized that he missed his ex-girlfriend and wanted her back, but by this time she had met someone new and made it clear she did not wish to resume her former relationship.

My patient's distress was extreme.

But he had also developed an obsession over the woman, telephoning her and sending text messages several times a day. He had difficulty sleeping and was in a constant state of anxiety.

He even sought help from a psychotherapist who advised him he would require three years of weekly therapy sessions to alleviate his symptoms. His own doctor dismissed the idea that he could be cured by therapy and instead prescribed the antidepressant Fluoxetine which had not helped at all.

When I saw this man for his first appointment, he was in a state of extreme agitation. His initial SUD—*subjective units of distress*—for general anguish was "10" on a scale of 0 to 10. Not only that, but his Fluoxetine medication was extremely toxic for him—as was some chocolate he had eaten earlier that day and oysters which were a frequent part of his diet. By using the 7-Second Toxin Treatment· and the algorithm for complex trauma with anger and guilt, his SUD eventually dropped to a "1. "

But our work was far from finished. Because not only did he exhibit the grief, obsession and feelings of rejection one might expect, he also tested quite high on the SUD scale for anger, jealousy, guilt, insomnia, low self-esteem, inadequacy, and helplessness. In each case, TFT brought his distress down to a "1."

By the end of the second session, my patient said he felt "elated" and that he "could not believe that he felt so good" after

---

∗ You can read more about the 7-Second Toxin Treatment at www.rogercallahan.com/pathways.

enduring months of mental torment. He realized he could gradually wean himself off Fluoxetine—using the 7-Second Treatment to counteract the toxic effects of the drug until he was off the medication completely.

Just two 45-minute sessions of TFT were required to bring about a complete cure—illustrating how some cases of love pain can be extremely complex and how TFT can succeed when other therapies fail.

—*Dr. Colin Barron*

* * *

In the case of love pain, the origin of additional symptoms such as anger, guilt, jealousy, insomnia, and obsession is clear. They all stem from a single romantic break-up.

But what about other complex traumas where, layer upon layer, the body uses new emotional traumas to mask previous ones? In such cases, the original underlying cause may actually be forgotten in the face of new grief, violence or emotional pain.

Read as one emergency responder discovers this aspect of emotional trauma for himself—and uses TFT to help unravel a lifetime of suffering for one brave woman.

The Day the Search Coordinator Found Herself

As a retired firefighter, I've suffered major emotional traumas in my career. I've witnessed devastation, grief and death—including the deaths of nine of my closest friends.

As a result, I became interested in Critical Incident Stress Management and soon became an authorized trauma trainer and earned a Certified Traumatologist credential from Florida State University. I was asked some 15 years ago if I thought my trauma training could be used by firefighters in unique cultural settings—such as that of the First Nations' communities in Canada. (In the U.S., we would call these communities "native

---

* Dr. Barron is a physician and is therefore qualified to assist a client in removing themselves from medication. You should never stop taking medication without a doctor's advice.

American" or "American Indian.") At the time, I believed it would. But what I didn't know then was how *harmful* this training would eventually be.

In these small and often remote communities, trauma happens on the same scale as in the rest of society. Road accidents, sudden death, drownings—they still happen, but the major difference is that psychological support is scarce when these traumas occur. Not only that, but as native populations meld into the greater national culture, their traditional practices and ritual healing methods become diminished. This means the impact of trauma can be even more severe for these unique people.

Unfortunately, when I first began using my formal CISM training for trauma relief, the methods I had learned to use often caused even greater distress because they triggered an *abreaction*—a "reliving" of the past experience in detail so vivid, the victims were shaken and often emerged less functional than before.

As an ethical person, I found it unacceptable to go into a community to teach, yet actually trigger trauma and then have nothing to assist in returning someone to their previous level of functioning or better. As a result, I had very nearly decided to quit teaching CISM in native communities.

Then I discovered TFT.

As I learned to use the tapping sequences, I was astounded at what they could accomplish. I now had a tool that I could use to help people through crisis and trauma. And hundreds of cases later, I'm even more convinced that TFT is an incredible discovery.

In one of my very first assignments, TFT rolled back years of emotional suffering for one woman whose job was actually to save *others* in her community. I met her when I was asked to put together a crisis response team to assist a remote village with a horrible loss. Two young men had gone out in winter weather and gotten lost. The community organized a search and spent days combing the territory looking for the teens—unfortunately without success. To date, they have not found any trace of the boys.

For the community of four hundred, it was a devastating loss. When I went in to do Critical Incident Stress Management, one of the first people I worked with was "Monica." She had been the search master, who stayed in the village to coordinate the search.

To say she was extremely distressed would have been an understatement. Yet within minutes, I used TFT to bring her SUD—*subjective units of distress*—down from a distraught "10" to a "1."

What I soon discovered, however, was that Monica had suffered numerous other traumas in her life—each one layering on top of the previous one to mask years of pain and suffering. And suffering she was. In fact, her story was a textbook example of complex trauma.

She explained that she was also diabetic and had experienced major vision loss as a result. She was nearly blind in one eye and had only 40% vision in the other.

Soon it emerged that—just like losing the teenage boys in the winter weather—she had lost an uncle who fell overboard from a fishing boat and was never found. At age 13, she was raped. With each TFT tapping sequence, we brought her distress down to "0"—yet as we resolved each past trauma, still another surfaced. Like peeling an onion, she had the most extensive trauma history I'd ever seen. Each event seemed to be covered over and blocked by another.

She even revealed that, when she was younger, her father had murdered her brother then committed suicide, leaving a note in which he had planned to kill Monica, too. Staying after school and returning home late was the only thing that had saved her. But she still arrived home to discover their deaths.

In every single case, her SUD was a "10"—and in every case, TFT reduced it to "0" using the complex trauma sequence.

After two hours of tapping, we were exhausted. When I offered to call a relative to help her home due to her bad eyesight, she replied, "I don't need him. I can see just fine now." Astonished, I asked her to explain, and she said that her eyesight prior to the search for the lost teens had been double what it had been recently. A diabetes specialist and opthamologist had both told her the problem was not physical, but most likely stress-related.

They could do nothing for her. But TFT did. Even months later, her vision and her release of the traumas was still good. It was one of my most gratifying experiences.

—*Bruce Ramsay*

* * *

Decades of work with people suffering from emotional trauma has convinced us that the mind is a delicate and fragile instrument. But it can be healed.

Just as TFT is being used every day by practitioners to relieve the suffering of victims by reorganizing the emotions attached to a traumatic event, these same practitioners themselves are asking, *Where else can TFT help?* They're finding new circumstances in which to apply TFT.

And they're finding themselves in some very unusual job assignments as a result. Victoria Yancey has been using TFT for years, but even she could not have predicted that she would be using it to relieve the horrors of trauma for children in the toughest neighborhoods of Philadelphia.

What's her unique job title? Take a look.

 ## Philadelphia's Guardian Angel

Students and families today are in crisis. From death-related tragedies such as suicide, homicide and illness—to equally life-changing traumas such as divorce and separation, foster care, abandonment, bullying, terrorism, domestic abuse and violence—it's no wonder children find it difficult to concentrate in school or feel comfortable in neighborhoods where a friend or family member has laid dead or wounded in the street.

For several years, as part of the Philadelphia school system, I've worked with parents and children in pain. The parents I meet have lost one child or several. Students have lost their mother, father or both parents. And families have lost loved ones in a city where violent death is common and the murder rate is the highest of any large city in America.

As the Philadelphia school district's Guardian Angel, my support to these children and their families includes participation in the funeral service or remembrance ceremony— a job which finds me in funeral homes, cemeteries and religious houses, sometimes attending as many as six funerals a day. But more often, I can be found beforehand in hospitals, schools and family homes comforting students and their families.

I know how difficult it is for students to return to school and see an empty desk, knowing that their classmate will not return. The students I meet are in a constant state of grief—crying, blaming, angry, numb, sad, lacking in appetite and suffering many other stress-related symptoms. Each handles grief in a different way.

That's where TFT can help.

At one funeral service I attended for a seven-year-old boy who had been savagely gunned down, family members found it difficult to contain their grief during the service. They wept openly throughout the service, sometimes screaming and even fainting in their grief. Many had to be carried out of the service. When the sisters of the deceased boy were carried out, I went to offer my services. They were experiencing such manifest grief that I wasn't sure they'd be able to focus on what I was saying.

I explained Thought Field Therapy and described how it might help them through the funeral service for their brother. Through their tears they expressed wanting to try TFT. They both agreed they were at the top of the SUD scale in rating their distress—a "10" in *subjective units of distress.*

As I led them through the tapping sequence, within minutes they reported feeling better with SUD scores of "0" and "1." They were actually smiling. They said they felt calmer and wanted to go back and join the other family members. I concluded the brief treatment with the floor-to-ceiling eye roll technique, and they rejoined their family in the church sanctuary. They did not suffer further that day. In fact, they were able to help others cope throughout the funeral ceremony.

When I saw them after the service, I asked how they were feeling.

"I don't know what happened, but after I tapped, I felt calmer and didn't feel like crying anymore," said one of the sisters.

Another had used one part of the tapping sequence with her young cousin who was very upset and angry, and "it seemed to help him," she said.

TFT is a powerful instrument to help those struggling with the detrimental effects of grief. It can be used to prevent the feelings of helplessness caused by grief. Thought Field Therapy is also compelling in recovery of those bereaved individuals suffering the anguish of loss, allowing them to function through their intense sorrow.

—Dr. Victoria Yancey

* * *

While it's understandable that students can fall victim to the emotional trauma of grief, few people expect professionals who deal with life and death, health and wellness, mental illness and emotional recovery to do so. Yet doctors—even mental health practitioners—can experience depression, grief and the symptoms of other emotional traumas, sometimes for years.

In this next story, TFT finds a supporter in an Oklahoma family practitioner who uses TFT to recover from his own despair, depression and grief. While well-meaning colleagues recommend that he "embrace his pain" in order to get better, we had a completely different approach in mind.

Doctors Get Sick, Too

Doctors aren't immune to depression, grief and despair. And while I've followed alternative therapies for years in helping my patients get better, somehow I never made getting well a top priority for me.

The truth is that I had suffered from chronic depression for years. It was almost as if other people with my condition were allowed to get well, but not me. I had nearly lost hope of ever finding a way out, until I attended a TFT diagnosis training and learned that TFT could erase depression with ease.

I volunteered to be measured first using the Heart Rate Variability (HRV) scanner—then be treated with the TFT depression algorithm so the effects of the treatment could be evaluated once again by the HRV scanner.

At first, my low HRV reading reflected my poor status.

Yet within five minutes of Dr. Callahan treating me, my depression of over seven years had vanished. I had a bright outlook. The change was almost beyond belief.

And my HRV chart reflected this improvement.

Thought Field Therapy helped me overcome my depressed state that day, but—to my sorrow—the real test of TFT was yet to come.

While attending an advanced training program for TFT practitioners, I learned of my daughter's sudden and unexpected death. She was my oldest daughter—my pride and joy. We had walked together four nights a week for five or six years. She was a beautiful person. Tragically though, she had suffered from chronic connective-tissue disease, and died suddenly while I was at the conference.

I was devastated.

I wanted to embrace the pain and experience the grief, so I was surprised when Roger Callahan told me it wasn't necessary to experience such anguish. He reassured me that it wasn't part of the TFT therapy to suffer, as it so often is with conventional therapies.

Roger worked with me that very same day, processing one by one the upsetting issues related to my trauma and grief. As we addressed each one, to my surprise, all of the intense pain I was feeling was reduced to just the sweet memories of my daughter while she lived and enormous compassion for her in death.

I completely changed my thinking about her death. I found that all of the sorrowful thoughts I had at the time were "safe" from then on. Later, though, as the weeks passed and innocent reminders of my daughter surfaced, I found myself slipping back into pain and despair.

In one particularly painful episode, a horse breeder who sold my daughter a horse last year asked if I wanted some photos of her. Of course, I did. It was a treasure beyond belief. Yet on seeing them, it was like being stabbed in the heart. I quickly called Roger and within minutes TFT eliminated all traces of pain.

As a practitioner, I've discovered that each aspect of a loss—whether a memory that surfaces or a friend who calls or a new piece of information you discover about your loved one and have to deal with following their death—has its own unique characteristics that need to be treated individually. If these disruptions are treated with TFT, they become compassionate memories within minutes—instead of a piercing arrow to the heart.

I've also discovered that the well-meaning advice I get from friends and professional colleagues who are unfamiliar with TFT is downright wrong. They've all recommended that I live with my pain, embrace it, feel it—and that recovering from my grief will take a year. Well, I discovered it doesn't take a year. It can take only minutes, in fact.

At times I wonder, *Maybe I'm not being as loyal as I should to my daughter and to her death.* And yet, at the same time, I really believe that people suffer far too long because they have not been exposed to TFT. I offer this in compassion and truth. I know that it goes against the common philosophy of the day, and I know that people who offer advice about the necessity of suffering over time have good intentions. But I see no need (and I have no desire) to continue in pain—especially when grief is so easily treated.

What a gift to humanity we could pass on by telling people that it's possible to care deeply for our loved ones in life, without having to suffer intensely for years at the loss of such precious and irreplaceable treasures.

—*H.E. Hagglund, MD*

* * *

Losing a loved one at any age is tragic, but the sudden loss of a child is even more emotionally traumatic. Intense grief in these situations would be considered normal and understandable, yet with TFT we find that suffering through grief is not necessary—*no matter the circumstances* in which your loved one died.

But what if your grief stems from actually seeing your loved one die before your very eyes?

In this next story, a certified psychologist from Canada helps his wife through a complex combination of grief, guilt, anger, fear and flashbacks after watching their family dog—and very nearly their son—die violently in a cougar attack.

 ## Grief, Guilt...Plus a Whole Lot More

It was a beautiful Autumn day when my wife Viv decided to go for a walk in a forested area close to our acreage in Calgary. Our one-year-old Samoyed dog Nakoda trotted happily by her side. One of our twin sons went, too, but decided to turn back after walking a short distance. To this day we are thankful that he did.

About 30 minutes into her walk, a flash of gold and tan bolted from behind a tree, knocking my wife to the ground and pouncing on Nakoda. Stunned and disoriented, Viv stood to witness a cougar mauling our beloved pet. The sights and sounds of the dog's death seared into Viv's brain as she began to take in what was happening. In a panic she fled the scene, feeling helpless and confused, as well as guilty for leaving Nakoda to the mercy of this wild animal.

She crashed through the hedge of a nearby farm, and the owner drove her home. During the short drive, Viv was panicked—not knowing if our son had made it home safely. Fortunately, he had and for the rest of the day, Viv and our twins stayed with the neighbor until I got home.

Until that day, we had no idea that cougars prowled near our acreage. We later discovered this particular cat had actually been prowling around our home!

When I arrived home, I heard the whole story. Not surprisingly, Viv was distraught. As a certified psychologist, I followed the standard protocols for defusing a critical incident, yet that night Viv was still tormented with flashbacks of the event—reliving the sights and sounds of Nakoda's last minutes. The next day we continued to talk and debrief the episode, but still, the second night was a repeat of the first. Viv was exhausted and in emotional pain. I had to get her some help.

As a psychologist in charge of an Employee Assistance Program for one of the largest employers in Calgary, I began to think about the options for referring Viv to a specialist in psychological trauma. Then it occurred to me that I should try something I had just learned at a seminar in Edmonton—Dr. Roger Callahan's Thought Field Therapy.

Viv was filled with guilt because she had left Nakoda at the mercy of the cougar. Other "what-ifs," including what could have happened to our son if he'd been there, left Viv feeling even more guilty. I looked up the algorithm for Complex Trauma with Guilt and asked Viv, though she could barely speak, to tune into her thought field. Her eyes filled with tears. And from the look on her face, I knew her SUD—*subjective units of distress*—were a "10." We tapped. She instantly dropped to an "8." As we continued tapping and eventually finished the treatment, she said she was incredibly tired and felt like sleeping. I 'cemented' with the floor-to-ceiling eye-roll and we went to bed.

Viv immediately fell asleep and did not wake up until morning. She was energetic, refreshed and back to her normal self. What a relief. This was my first, real-life application of TFT, and what an impact it had on our family.

But would it hold? I knew about toxins and how a toxin could undo the results.

However, six months after the attack, with no more nightmares and no negative emotional residue, Viv and I decided to walk together and re-visit the attack site. Not far from the site, the cougar had dragged Nakoda's body and buried it at the foot of a tree. To my horror, as we approached, we found bits of fur, bones and two front paws strewn about the forest as a result of other animals (coyotes probably) having dug up bits of the body!

I watched closely to see how Viv would react.

Incredibly, she was just very matter of fact—describing again what happened, where she was, where the cougar came from and where Nakoda was mauled. But there was absolutely no further evidence of the emotional pain she had experienced six months earlier. I was amazed and relieved.

A year later, Viv still has no ill effects since the evening we tapped using TFT. I am most grateful to Dr. Roger Callahan for discovering this incredible treatment. After a year, the effect of Viv's TFT treatment has still held. And I expect now that it always will.

—Martin Law, RPsych

* * *

Grief can emerge from any kind of loss—whether it's the death of someone close, a romantic break-up, the loss of a business, loss of a friend, a change in residence, losing at a competitive event, even a necessary surgery that causes the "loss" of a physical function. In this unusual story, unresolved grief from such a surgery 25 years earlier was the cause of present-day pain and suffering—both emotional and physical.

A Different Kind of Loss

A fellow colleague came to see me, worried that he may be developing prostate cancer. He was already suffering from prostate problems, and had been to a doctor who ordered tests for prostate enlargement, renal function and cardiac symptoms.

He had been suffering from stress for over a year, but had a happy family life. I asked him if there was anything in his past that might have left trauma in the affected part of his body. He could not recall anything, so I checked for trauma and found none present. I questioned him further and gave him time to really think about the answer.

Then he remembered that he had had a vasectomy 25 years earlier—and that it had taken him a year to get over it.

I suddenly had a clear image of grief. Further testing immediately revealed that it was the emotion present. I asked him for an SUD estimate, and he realized with shock that it was at a "6" even decades after the surgery.

I treated him with TFT and within a couple of minutes his SUD dropped to "0." He suddenly said he felt completely different.

Unconsciously, he had been grieving all these years for the loss of part of him. He had never gotten over this loss, as he felt the operation had been the worst decision of his life.

Since the TFT treatment, however, he reports that his whole outlook has changed, and he is now reacting to everything in a much more positive way.

We can grieve over the loss of a job or a house—even an object that we have misplaced. But people can also grieve over the loss of a body part or the function of a body part, which is where my client had been stuck for 25 years. Mourning is not just limited to the loss of loved ones or pets. We can grieve over anything that is lost to us. What may appear insignificant to others, can be a person's whole universe. It is the client's perception that is important.

—Ildiko Scurr

* * *

When we talk about Thought Field Therapy and emotional trauma—grief, anger, guilt and rejection—people often assume that our clients and patients are all adults.

But emotional trauma can strike children, too.

And when it does, it is a heartbreaking sight. Today, in virtually every society we visit around the world, we see evidence of emotional distress in the faces of children. It isn't just war or poverty that causes this emotional trauma, but everyday instances like fighting parents, bullying on the playground, a favorite toy that is stolen at school, and most especially, violent images they see on television—or even in their own neighborhoods.

In this story of a school counselor who uses TFT with children, two youngsters get relief with TFT. But even more interesting to note is that with TFT, students rarely resist by saying, *This won't work* or *This seems weird.*

They just want to feel better.

Thought Field Therapy Goes to School

"Kevin," a six-year-old boy who I have known since he began kindergarten, asked his teacher if he could see the counselor. When he came in, he sat looking dejected.

"My mom and step-dad had a fight, and my step-dad left," Kevin said in a low voice.

As we talked about the events of the previous evening, he told how he was in bed when he heard the two of them fighting. His stepfather had left and was not coming back. Before Kevin left for school that morning, his mom had talked to him about the changes that would occur. Kevin told me that he was sad.

Unfortunately, this was not the first time I had seen him for troubles at home.

The first time we met, his mother and stepfather had had a fight. Kevin came to me because he could not do his schoolwork. I treated Kevin with the anxiety algorithm then.

Today was something more momentous, however.

When I asked Kevin what could we do to help him feel better, he looked at me and started tapping the side of his hand. He remembered that part of the treatment from five months earlier.

When asked how upset he was this morning on a 1-10 scale, Kevin responded that he was a "10." I asked Kevin to tap the side of his hand, saying three times, *I'm a great kid even though I have this problem.* We followed with the anxiety algorithm and brought his SUD—*subjective units of distress*—down to a "0." Kevin reported he was feeling better and wanted to go back to class.

After lunch, I went to Kevin's classroom and asked him how he was doing. He was busy writing, so just smiled and gave me a thumbs up. When I followed up with him the next day and the following week, each time he reported that all was well with him.

"Janice" is another girl at the same school, though she was not one of my usual clients. When I asked her what had brought her to see me, she reported having nightmares about the toys in her bedroom attacking her. I asked if she had discussed this with her parents, to which she replied that her mother had told her to go to bed and that the nightmares would go away.

The bad dreams had started over the weekend. By now, it was Wednesday. I suspected that she had seen a movie or something on television that might have triggered this response in her. By now, her SUD was a "10" when she thought about going into her room and about the stuffed animals attacking her. Using the phobia algorithm, I talked her three times through the tapping sequence and we were able to reduce her fear to zero.

By the next morning, she said that all was well. The following week, she was still sleeping soundly—with no more nightmares or fear of going into her bedroom.

—*Nicholas Seferlis, MS, LCPC*

* * *

Thought Field Therapy is an ideal technique for people who want relief from emotional trauma, but are fearful of entering into "formal" psychotherapy. They don't want to feel broken or sick or as if they may have a serious disorder. TFT is non-threatening, does not require medication, is fast and does no harm.

It is also a technique that easily crosses the barriers of culture and language. As long as a patient or client can visually follow the tapping sequence by the practitioner, the patient or client can experience relief. TFT is also sympathetic with local customs, traditional healing and grief rituals, and with local medical procedures.

In this story of trauma and grief in Mexico, a TFT practitioner uses the tapping sequences with Spanish-speaking parents who have suffered the loss of a child.

South of the Border, It's Terapia Campo Mental

As an educator in Colorado and also fluent in Spanish, I was delighted to be asked to work with a therapy group in Mexico City helping parents whose children have died.

The group's leader, Connie Bravo, is an advocate of TFT and offered to host me if I would provide *Terapia Campo Mental* to her group. I seized the opportunity to practice TFT in Spanish.

Connie forewarned me about the parents—about their emotional states, their attitudes and resentments. Some were apprehensive. Others had mixed emotions about TFT. Yet as I talked about the pressure points to be used, I could feel the parents' resistance fading. To them, TFT was non-threatening, simple and culturally acceptable.

When I asked for volunteers, a middle-aged husband and wife were the first to try TFT. They were the parents of two teenaged sons who had tragically died in the same road accident.

We tapped for Complex Trauma with Anger and Guilt. They were in a very emotional state, but after tapping, relaxed from a "10" on the SUD scale to a "0." For the first time, they said, they felt relief and less tension.

Other parents volunteered and as I treated them one at a time, I heard their heartrending stories. By the end of the session, all seemed less aggressive, less angry, very calm, a bit perplexed and in awe of the results of TFT. Connie told me later that it was the first time in a long while that these parents had felt any "good" emotions—so riddled were they with guilt, trauma, anger and rage.

Even one angry, isolated, resistant and enraged mother—who thought that TFT was quackery—got relief of an unexpected nature.

Along with her Complex Trauma symptoms, she was also suffering from agonizing pain on the side of her face. Her head was tender to the touch, much like an agonizing toothache that causes pain to travel from the jaw to the temple.

First, we tapped for pain. TFT easily brought it down to "0." In astonishment, she touched the side of her face without feeling severe pain. She attempted a slight smile and allowed me to administer the TFT sequence for Complex Trauma with Anger and Guilt. Her SUD immediately dropped to a "2," and for the rest of the session she was relaxed and calm, socializing with the rest of the parents. She even refrained from smoking incessantly which she had done in every other group session. Other parents commented that I must have had quite an impact on her, as they had never seen her smile, laugh, hug, or be free of complaint in all the years they had been meeting.

—*Oneyda Maestas*

Tapping Away Emotional Trauma

You'll find videos that step you through the complete tapping sequences for grief, love pain and other emotional traumas at our website:

www.rogercallahan.com/pathways

5

Chapter Five:
Eliminating Phobias and
Other Controlling Disorders

Thirty years ago, my very first TFT patient was "Mary," a young mother of two who suffered from an extreme phobia of water. It kept her nearly paralyzed with fear—unable to pursue even the most basic activities if they involved water or brought her near to water. Bathing her children was impossible for her, and even her own brief showers were extremely stressful. Leaving the house in a rainstorm absolutely terrified her. And her nightmarish dreams of being dropped into the ocean all added up to the most severe water phobia I had seen in my practice up until that time.

But it was Mary who helped me discover the miracle of tapping.

Sitting around my pool one day after a year of therapy with me, she became nauseous at her fear of being near the water.

Then, I had an idea.

Knowing that the Chinese had used acupuncture for over 5,000 years to correct blockages and energy flows through the body's meridians, I asked Mary to tap a few times under her eye—which I knew was the location of the end point of the stomach meridian.

Suddenly Mary exclaimed, "It's gone!" and made a beeline for the pool—bending down to splash water on her face.

That night, Mary decided to test her phobia cure by driving to the ocean in a rare California rainstorm. Wading into the surf until the water reached waist-high, she remained completely free of her fear—and still does even decades later.

It was at that point I knew a stunning discovery had been handed to me.

In some of our favorite stories of life after a TFT treatment, phobic patients talk about their new-found freedom and how fast TFT works for phobias.

Fear of Public Speaking Is the #1 Phobia

Studies reveal that some people would rather die than speak before an audience. This fear is known as *glossophobia*—a term that comes from the Greek words *glossa* meaning "tongue" and *phobia* meaning "fear." Research reveals that public speaking is the number one fear most common across the globe.

In fact, surveys show that fear of public speaking actually outnumbers the fear of death.

Why?

Because when compared to death, the need to speak in public impacts virtually every aspect of daily life.

In my career as an instructor and an educational consultant, I often teach public speaking to parents, community groups, and teenagers, as well as to university students. As a consultant, I work with individuals and corporate workgroups to help develop public-speaking skills in their employees.

The thought of public speaking can cause the most confident individual to break out in a cold sweat with visual shaking of hands and legs. Having to speak before an audience can cause an otherwise poised leader to stumble through an oratory with a dry throat and quivering voice. In working with individuals, small groups and classes, I find that Thought Field Therapy is a powerful tool for reducing and eliminating anxiety of public speaking.

At some point in life, almost every one of us must communicate in a public manner. This is especially true of students and those in the workforce.

Difficulty in public speaking can negatively effect careers, self-confidence and student grades. Students have professed that public-speaking classes are among the most difficult they experience in school. Considering this knowledge, I began using Thought Field Therapy with students and clients experiencing difficulty in public speaking.

---

* Studies have been cited by Stephen Lucas in his book *The Art of Public Speaking* (McGraw Hill Publishers); Jim Peterson in his article "Speech Topics Help, Advice & Ideas" at www.speech-topics-help.com/index.html; and by J. Dan Rothwell in his book *In the Company of Others: An Introduction to Communication* (McGraw Hill Publishers).

What are some of the symptoms of *glossophobia*—or fear of public speaking? Dry mouth, nervous laughter, forgetting what to say, shaky hands and legs, touching hair, shaky voice, nausea, feelings of embarrassment, wanting to run, hide hands in pockets, playing with ring or jewelry, quivering lips, stammering and just an overall bad feeling are common.

After explaining that Thought Field Therapy is a self-help technique consisting of tapping sequences designed to eliminate the negative emotions relating to public speaking, I have my clients rate their anxiety. I ask them to think or attune to the level of distress when thinking about having to make a presentation before an audience. The individual then rates their public speaking anxiety in Subjective Units of Distress (SUD) from 0 to 10, zero being no disturbance and 10 meaning the highest level of disturbance. I then lead them through the TFT tapping sequence for anxiety, concluding with a floor-to-ceiling "eye roll."

What I have found is that, though many individuals are apprehensive about using TFT at the beginning, they work through the process and find themselves becoming calmer and less tense. Within minutes, smiles appear instead of tense faces or tears when thinking of having to speak in public. Students gain a clarity of thought while in front of an audience—plus they have the ability to remember the order of their speech and what it is they wanted to say. As one participant put it, "I no longer think about being nervous. I just think about what I have to say. My mind just seems clearer."

In other words, students who use Thought Field Therapy prior to giving their speech are able to concentrate on the context of their presentation, rather than being bothered by those debilitating behaviors that prevented them from speaking in public in the past. I've also noticed—after using TFT—that students are often the first to volunteer to give their presentations (and volunteer to help their peers). Those I teach in a corporate setting reveal that Thought Field Therapy has helped them improve their public speaking—and because of this, they've had more opportunities for career advancement.

Thought Field Therapy not only increases confidence and self-assurance while speaking in public, it helps fearful speakers concentrate on the context of their speech with superb clarity of thought—rather than focusing on debilitating behaviors that prevent effective public speaking.

—*Dr. Victoria Yancey*

* * *

A phobia is a persistent fear without a logical reason—usually having to do with a harmless object or situation. Ironically, most people who have phobias realize how unrealistic their fear is, which in turn makes them feel foolish and embarrassed. Nevertheless, their phobias continue to disrupt their lives, their relationships—and even their careers.

In our next story, one woman suffered sheer agony in her chosen career because she feared speaking to groups. Presenting blueprints and design plans nearly immobilized her. Finally, when faced with the prospect of speaking at a prominent industry conference which would boost her standing in her industry—she knew she had to get help.

After exhausting all other possibilities for a cure of her public speaking phobia, she finally discovered TFT.

Afraid of My Own Shadow

Growing up, I was horribly afraid of my own shadow. I had a fear of strangers. Public places left me shaking. As a little child, I used to hide under my bed when company came—and if we went out of the house, I was stuck to my mom as a third leg. I never knew what caused the fear. My parents knew of no trauma that had happened to me. Their conclusion was simply that I was a very shy child.

Once in school, I'd make myself sick worrying about giving a speech in front of the class or singing in a choir recital in front of other parents. To adapt, I chose to be the person behind the scenes and not the one in the spotlight. Still, my body would shake, my heart would race, and my mind would freeze as I turned bright red in the face.

Any new environment or change would be painful for me, as I worried myself to the point of exhaustion.

By the time I started working for a living—in a job and later, owning my own business—I knew I had to get rid of this ridiculous fear. I tried everything I could think of—therapy, acupuncture, Reiki, hypnosis, desensitizing myself by forcing myself to go to public places, self-help books and audio tapes.

While those things did help—the anxiety of speaking in front of people remained. Not only that, but eventually I owned a commercial and residential interior-renovation company that required multiple presentations of proposals and blueprints in front of customers. Trying to be a successful female in what is typically a "man's" business gave me the incentive to face my fears and do these presentations anyway. Though I was often sick to my stomach before presenting to a construction board or discussion panel, somehow I managed to get through, even though I was a nervous wreck.

To make matters worse, I also fell victim to "Sick Building Syndrome"—where the toxins in some buildings were so pervasive, it overloaded my immune system to the point where I became very sick indeed. Through many different types of conventional and alternative medical methods, I regained my health. It soon became my passion to educate people about the dangers of toxins that lurk in our homes and workplaces.

But one problem remained.

I was afraid to speak in public about this topic that I had become so passionate about.

Then I met Joanne and Roger Callahan.

For the first time I was introduced to Thought Field Therapy—this "weird" tapping thing. I purchased the book Tapping the Healer Within and a whole new world opened up to me. I knew I had finally found a safe and natural way to eliminate my fears so that I could live the full life I desired.

Six months later, I was asked to present as part of a panel at the Facility Manager Convention in Baltimore. The topic was

"How Air Quality and Environmental Quality Affects Employee Productivity"—a topic I could easily and passionately speak about.

Without thinking, I agreed to do it.

But when I hung up the phone, it hit me. This was a national convention attended by thousands of people. I had never given a speech like this before, let alone in front of an audience that size. I was nearly paralyzed with fear.

In the two weeks I had left to design my presentation and get to the convention, I used the anxiety-stress algorithm from Dr. Callahan's book. Yet here I was—the day before the presentation and at home... a nervous wreck. I couldn't stop shaking and my voice was wavering. I had a migraine. I just knew I couldn't speak feeling like this.

So I called Dr. Callahan for a private session to overcome my fear of public speaking. Over the phone, Dr. Callahan created a specific tapping sequence just for my immediate problem. As I did the series of taps he gave me, I could feel the amazing changes in my body. The shaking started to subside, my heart started beating regularly, the red rash started to clear up within minutes of doing the tapping. Dr. Callahan lowered my distress from a "10" down to a "4" in just 15 minutes.

Next thing I knew, however, it was back up to a 10. I was feeling horrible again.

Dr. Callahan asked what just happened. I told him I hadn't moved from the spot in my bedroom. He told me *something* had changed and asked if anyone had come into the room. I told him my son had come in to get something he needed.

"Was he wearing any cologne?" Dr. Callahan asked.

I replied that he always wears this one brand of cologne which bothers me. Dr. Callahan checked and said that my son's cologne was so toxic to me that it threw me into a reversal which brought the fear back in force.

Dr. Callahan had me do a breathing exercise to neutralize the toxin in my system. Within minutes, I started feeling better. Then my husband walked into the room and—having been near enough to my son for his clothes to pick up a residual scent of the cologne—my husband caused a further relapse of my fear.

Once again, I did the breathing exercise, followed by the tapping sequence. After 35 minutes, TFT reduced my fear from a "10" to a "1." Of course I took the tapping notes with me to the convention, and just before I went on stage, I snuck into the ladies room and tapped through the sequence again.

Needless to day, speaking for the first time as a calm, confident and passionate presenter, it was one of the most amazing experiences of my career. Even when they changed the room location at the last minute, changed the stage set-up from my practice run-through, improperly loaded my videos so one of them didn't play during my speech—I still felt confident, focused and calm. Even at the end of my speech, when an Environmental Hygienist in the audience challenged me about some points in my speech, I held my own.

But more importantly, I felt empowered and self-assured.

At that point, I knew my lifelong crippling fear of speaking was a thing of the past. I was now free to go out and educate people on how to build healthier lives at home and in their workplace through an awareness of toxins and their affect on our bodies.

TFT is a wonderful, safe and natural way to eliminate fears and anxieties. It opened up a whole new world for me.

—*Christina Mayhew*

* * *

Sometimes the fear of public speaking can actually stifle a person's career or potential for future success. One example is a former client of ours, a woman golfer on the pro circuit. She contacted us because she felt her golf career was being limited, since every time she would be close to winning a tournament, she would start worrying about having to speak to the media if she won.

She would tighten up and begin missing shots. And, believe it or not, after performing badly in the tournament, she was actually relieved because she did not have to speak to the media or do any interviews. She knew this fear was limiting her performance and career opportunities. Each year, she had promised herself she would overcome this limitation.

She contacted us for help, and within just a couple of sessions, there was no further trace of her fear. Shortly after those sessions, we watched her on television, giving a calm and poised interview with the media, after she had just won the day's tournament.

Of course, while the fear of public speaking is the most common phobia, other phobias also abound and are often the result of a seemingly harmless, but lasting traumatic episode from childhood.

In this next story—of a woman who became fearful of flying creatures as a toddler—TFT releases her lifelong fear of birds so she can visit the historic market district of Old San Juan.

Let's take a look:

From Merely Coping to Really Living

Recently my wife and I had the occasion to visit the old section of San Juan, Puerto Rico—a beautifully preserved historical site near the ocean. We met a lady in her thirties there who had had a lifelong fear of birds, a phobia she determined had originated when she was a toddler. As a small child, she had been attempting to hold a "moth or butterfly" and it frightened her as it flew into her face many times. As she recalled, she became afraid of flying creatures after that incident, birds being included in that category.

I told her I might be able to help her eliminate or reduce the fear, and she was most agreeable if the process did not cause her undue distress.

I briefly explained TFT and proceeded to treat her—first for the painful memory, and then with the basic TFT sequence for phobia.

Within moments, she no longer felt discomfort while thinking about birds. I then pointed out that—since only exposure to reality would tell if the treatment was complete—we needed to encounter some birds. Since she and her friend, as well as my wife and I, were planning to tour the old section of the city that day, I surmised a test would be possible.

When we arrived in Old San Juan, there were birds literally everywhere! Perched in the trees, flocking on the pavement, screeching after stray crumbs from tourists—the air was filled with birds and their cacophony of noise.

While the woman indicated some discomfort, it was in no way extreme. I then offered her some additional treatment, and within seconds she reported feeling even greater relief.

As she approached the flocks of birds, she exclaimed, "I would never have been able to do this before! I could never walk this close to birds before."

She then noted with obvious calm and clarity that she was also *much more aware of birds* than she had ever been before. As she surveyed the area, pointing out the ever-present multitude of birds of Old San Juan, she realized she had previously shut down much of her awareness of birds as a kind of protective device and now no longer required that coping mechanism.

But while years of distraction may have helped this lady cope, it did nothing to resolve the bird phobia, which was successfully cured in moments with TFT.

—Fred P. Gallo, PhD

* * *

Just like the fear of birds, phobias can develop around all kinds of animals—but most especially around spiders and snakes. Perhaps it's because they're visually disturbing, dangerous and unpredictable. But as intense as these phobias can be, the treatment is as simple as with "lesser" phobias.

In this next story of a lifelong fear of snakes, one woman changes from TFT skeptic to true believer.

Fear of Snakes Causes Severe Physical Distress

Having a young brother that frequently brought home snakes made my life uneasy at a very early age. Family camping trips were never fun, as I was always fearful of encountering a snake—dead or alive—only to have my brother tease me by threatening to throw it at me. Looking back now, I can see the controlling effect this fear of snakes had on me.

Spring was always the most difficult time. My fear of snakes coming out of hibernation kept me from doing things in the yard or working in the garden. When chaperoning my children's annual field trip to the zoo, I would wait outside the snake house while another mother went inside—including my group with hers.

Words simply can't express the depth of fear I felt at just the mention of the word "snake."

When I was first approached with Thought Field Therapy as a way out of my phobia, I was frankly skeptical. It would not take long—perhaps five to fifteen minutes of my time—I was told. They even said it was painless!

I laughed it off and walked away—not because I didn't believe it, but because I did not want to face my fear. Two weeks went by before I was again asked if I would like to get rid of my fear of snakes.

Finally I consented—under one condition. If I had to touch a snake or have it be present in the same room, no deal! Assured there would not be any snakes involved, I tentatively began.

When told at first to think about snakes and rate my fear on a scale of 1 to 10, the mere thought of snakes sent me into a tailspin. I felt instantly sick to my stomach, my heart began beating rapidly, I felt faint, and my head began to ache.

Realizing I had invited this physical distress by allowing the treatment, I was even more frightened. As far as I was concerned, "10" was not high enough to measure my distress and physical pain.

Then the therapy began.

At first, it was difficult for me to concentrate on the instructions because of the physical pain I was experiencing. But as the minutes ticked quickly by, the transformation in my mind and body was astounding. I felt as if a heavy weight had been lifted from my shoulders—as if I had just awakened refreshed and content from a deep sleep. To my utter disbelief, within minutes my fear of snakes was gone.

Not only can I now say the word "snake" without suffering my usual physical distress, I can look at pictures of them, watch movies about them and read books about them with my grandchildren.

Dr. Callahan's technique for ridding people of their phobias is so unique, I wish I had been introduced to TFT long ago. Those few minutes changed my life.

—*Rosemarie Solarz*

* * *

It's no secret that phobias can control a person's life—by limiting the places they go, the people they see, the environments they're willing to enter into, even access to the necessities of life.

In this story of multiple fears and phobias, one patient gets relief from an unusual source—her *dentist* who is also a trained TFT practitioner.

Fear of Heights Just 2½ Feet Off the Ground

When "Bonnie" came to me with a broken tooth that needed repair, I didn't realize how nervous and tense she was until it was time to administer the anesthetic. She had a fear of needles, she told me, and I immediately said I could help her overcome the fear by using the TFT sequence for phobias.

As I started to raise the dental chair to guide her through the sequence, however, she fearfully asked me to stop. She was terrified of heights, it turns out, and was clearly panicked by the rising chair. Interestingly, the dental chair was just 2½ feet off the ground—lower than her head would have been had she been standing up. I decided to work on her fear of heights first since it appeared to be a greater stressor. Also, I knew we would get immediate feedback simply by raising and lowering the chair.

In my dental office, I usually tap on the patient while they concentrate on their fear or traumatic thought. I find this quicker and less confusing than asking the patient to tap out the sequence on themselves. Before the actual treatment, I always show the patient the spots that I will tap on, so the patient knows what to expect.

As I described the spots to Bonnie—at first touching the Gamut spot lightly once—she looked at me surprised and said, "What did you do? I feel more relaxed."

I thought to myself, *Wow, if just touching the spots had such a rapid effect on her, Bonnie's phobias would be easy to treat.*

I asked her to think of her fear of heights, which she rated at a "9" on the SUD scale *(subjective units of distress)*. After a few minutes of tapping, her rating went down to a "6." While the fear of heights was still present, Bonnie continued to say how very relaxed and calm she was. After a few more minutes of tapping, we eventually reduced her SUD to a "3."

"I feel very calm," she said.

At that point, I was able to raise the dental chair as high as it would go—about four feet off the ground. While Bonnie still felt somewhat fearful, it was nothing like her fear had been in the beginning. We spent just 20 minutes doing these procedures, after which we decided to proceed with the planned dental work.

Working on a much more relaxed patient this time, I realized how tense Bonnie had actually been on her previous visits. It was now easy to complete the dental procedures. He tongue was still and she did not display distress with me working in her mouth. When we were done, she commented on how good she felt and how unusual it was for her to feel good after a dental appointment.

I asked her to use her ladder when she got home, since she had previously mentioned she could climb only to the second step.

Two days later, I called Bonnie. She had climbed her ladder without fear. Plus, she had also been able to stop taking her normal Tagamet dosage for stomach problems since her TFT session. Even two weeks later, acidic foods like coffee, tomato soup and others couldn't cause a return of her stomach upset.

She reported being calmer, too, and said that—mentally—she was able to leave her work at the office. But more than that, whenever she felt nervous, Bonnie used the TFT anxiety sequence for instant relief.

—*Michael Sills, DDS*

* * *

Just like fear of heights, fear of flying, too, is a common phobia that can be treated with Thought Field Therapy. In fact, our original *5-Minute Phobia Cure·*—developed 30 years ago—is used around the world by air passengers who panic at the thought of lifting off from the runway into thin air.

In 2010, Roger treated actress Whoopi Goldberg who later detailed her TFT cure on the morning talk show, *The View.* And TFT is a key component of the fear of flying program offered in Great Britain by Virgin Atlantic Airways.

To see how easy it is to overcome fear of flying, read this heartwarming story about a 10-year-old boy and what could have been a disastrous first ride on an airplane.

30,000 Feet of Excitement

While flying to Phoenix one day, a 10-year-old boy and his father were sitting next to me on the plane. As the flight attendant closed the hatch and prepared for take-off, I noticed the boy in the beginning stages of a panic attack.

As his heart rate increased and his breathing became shallow, the boy's father grew increasingly anxious—uncertain about what to do for his son.

I asked the boy if he was afraid. "Yes sir," he replied. "I hear we are going to be flying at 30,000 feet, and I've never been in a plane before."

∗ Read more about the 5-Minute Phobia Cure which can be used to treat fear of flying and other phobias at www.rogercallahan.com/pathways.

His agitation became even more extreme as the aircraft began to taxi out onto the runway. Because of my concern, I turned to his father and asked if I could help.

When the father agreed, I told the boy I would be gently tapping on him and that—while I did so—he should think about his fears. Using two fingers, I began tapping under his eye, over his eye, and on his collar bone. When I asked him if he felt better, he replied "Yes, sir."

Because of the cramped quarters, I wasn't able to tap out the complete sequence. But I did continue the eye and collar bone tapping, and by the time the plane reached the runway, the youngster was completely over his anxiety. In fact, he was excited about the take-off and the flight to Phoenix.

I monitored him throughout the one hour flight, and he showed no further signs of anxiety. His father couldn't stop thanking me. The TFT fear of flying sequence turned what could have been a horrible experience into an exciting adventure for a brave little boy.

—Shad Meshad, MSW, LCSW, CPS

* * *

If a 10-year-old boy could be helped with Thought Field Therapy, could another 10-year-old *actually practice* the simple TFT sequences and bring relief to others?

The answer is yes.

In this captivating story of a young girl who was attacked by a dog and learned the healing powers of TFT first-hand, we discover that TFT is so easy, even a child can learn it, understand it and successfully use it on herself and others.

Plus, as we've already discovered, TFT has no side effects. So tapping out the sequences "incorrectly" or "incompletely" can do no harm.

Curing Phobias...It's Child's Play

Jamie, my 10-year-old daughter, may be the youngest Thought Field Therapy practitioner ever. She became interested in TFT after my family attended a diagnostic training with Dr. Roger Callahan. After that, she saw me treat her aunt for fear of dogs, and was further intrigued.

Three months later, she herself was attacked and bitten on the face by a large boxer and went into shock. I was on the scene within minutes and used the TFT trauma sequence on her, which not only brought her out of shock, it resulted in her color returning—and her getting up and playing normally, without residual fear, nightmares or ever bringing up the issue again.

Then a few weeks later, she was in my office and wanted to watch the "Introduction to Thought Field Therapy" videotape. As she watched, she surprised me by taking notes, but never explained what her intent was in doing so.

Shortly thereafter, she asked me for the phobia sequence and I learned very quickly how she planned to use it.

I have a three-year-old niece who was terrified of dogs—especially the three large dogs on our property. She would not let me treat her because she is also terrified of large males with beards.

My 10-year-old daughter took her aside and treated her without us knowing. While my niece was previously a toddler who would run away screaming from any dog, we happened to glance out the window one day while her family was visiting and saw her alone on the grass, holding our 120-pound Rottweiler by its leash.

We learned that day that TFT is so easy, even a 10-year-old can use it successfully.

—*Stephen P. Daniel*

* * *

Phobias are just one example of disorders that can control a person's lifestyle, relationships, job prospects and even their livelihood. Stories abound of management candidates who were passed over for jobs because they were unable to present proposals to clients, run weekly staff meetings, make sales calls or perform other duties due to crippling social phobias, fear of public speaking, fear of driving or other disorders which are simple to eliminate with Thought Field Therapy.

Could fears, phobias and controlling disorders be limiting your life? All too often we see patients in our practice who are prevented from living life fully due to social phobias, bipolar conditions, avoidance behaviors, situational anxiety, hypervigilance and other controlling behaviors.

TFT can provide relief—as we see in this brief case history from *just one TFT practitioner* who works with patients and clients who are clearly at the end of their rope.

 12 Cases. 12 Lives Changed with TFT.

As a psychologist working with a variety of patients, I've found that Thought Field Therapy brings about amazing changes in their mental state, their ability to function, and in their overall outlook for recovery.

Below are just a few examples of TFT in action—changing lives and improving outcomes:

Case 1—One patient of mine, a young woman, had all the symptoms of severe social phobia including stammering, being unable to speak in social situations, trembling, heart palpitations, increased perspiration, and a flushed face. With TFT treatment, her SUD *(subjective units of distress)* decreased from a "10" to a "0."

She was able to confidently present herself for a job interview, and—after repeating the sequence in the restroom when she found out she was going to be interviewed by three people instead of the one she had anticipated—she did so well in the interview that she got the job.

Case 2—Another patient, a young adult male with fear of heights, appeared in my office trembling with apprehension. He was pale looking, had cold hands and feet, and routinely experienced heart palpitations, shallow breathing, stomach knots, jaw and shoulder tightness, and dizziness. His SUD decreased from a "10" to a "0" with TFT.

Not only was he able to go to the upper floors of high-rise buildings afterward, a similar fear of driving was eliminated, too, thereby improving his marriage as his self-confidence increased.

Case 3—A young man with mild ongoing depression, obsessive-compulsive disorder and social phobia told me he "felt miserable." He was despondent, often had death wishes, lacked self-confidence, and was even experiencing chest and stomach pains. Not only that, but he clearly had difficulty focusing, exhibited facial and body tension, and had the dejected countenance and posture of someone who is continually sad.

TFT easily reduced his SUD from a "10" to a "0." And while his physical symptoms retreated—that is, his facial expressions, color, and body posture shifted from tense and dejected to relaxed and smiling—more importantly, his mental images and thoughts shifted from despair to optimism.

Case 4—Another patient, a young man, suffered from depression along with irritability, resentment, and anger. He was less functional than he should have been and had a constant scowling expression, tensed and hunched shoulders, and taut muscles. I used Thought Field Therapy to lower his SUD from a "10" to a "0." Not only that, but his intimidating appearance softened, and he relaxed to an amiable, affable, focused and goal-oriented individual.

Case 5—One patient of mine, a middle-aged woman with bipolar disorder felt as though she was "spinning out of control." She'd had to discontinue her medication that stabilized her mood because it caused medical complications. She had racing thoughts, mild agitation, difficulty focusing, impulsive feelings. Yet with TFT, her SUD decreased to "0." She calmed down, could focus more clearly, and was able to begin addressing her other problems.

Case 6—A young woman patient suffered from post-traumatic stress disorder. In addition, she had depression, anxiety and chronic fatigue syndrome. Her other symptoms were even more severe and disruptive—flashbacks, nightmares, hypervigilance, excessive startle reaction, avoidance behaviors, muscular pain, fatigue, and headaches. With TFT, I was able to reduce the PTSD symptoms from "10" to "0" along with her secondary symptoms of depression and anxiety. I used specific TFT sequences for her fatigue, muscular pain and chronic headaches which decreased to a "0" or "3" on the SUD scale (*subjective units of distress*).

Case 7—A middle-aged man came to see me with extreme anxiety about a major presentation he was about to give. Not only was he experiencing mild dizziness, but he also had cold hands, lack of focus and memory problems. His SUD immediately dropped from a "10" to a "0" with TFT. Additionally, his apprehension and anxiety shifted to eagerness to present his materials. His dizziness and cold hands evaporated. And he maintained clear focus and good functioning memory during his presentation.

Case 8—Another patient, a young woman with major depressive disorder, entered my office feeling irritable and "on edge." She wasn't sleeping well and had difficulty concentrating. TFT immediately gave her relief—dropping her SUD from a "10" to a "0" and changing her demeanor to a laughing and carefree woman, chuckling at the humorous side of the predicament she was coping with at the time.

Case 9—A patient who smoked more than three packs a day eventually saw her smoking habit compound her medical problems. Unfortunately, she felt she was unable and unwilling to give up smoking despite the health consequences. She was more than willing to learn the TFT stop-smoking procedure for use in the future—if and when she did decide to quit smoking. While she was in the process of learning the procedure, her cravings for cigarettes dropped from a "10" to a "0." She immediately threw the three packs of cigarettes she had in her purse into the trash can before leaving my office.

Case 10—A woman who suffered from a severe social phobia and social anxiety to the point that her hands dripped with perspiration, got immediate relief with TFT as the perspiration in her hands dried up.

Case 11—Another patient with major depressive disorder and an anxiety disorder had extreme cravings for alcohol which she had used to dull her anxiety symptoms. Her cravings—at a 9 on the SUD scale suddenly decreased to 0 with TFT. Not only that, but her anxiety symptoms of chest discomfort, increased perspiration, palpitations, tension in her jaw, neck and back, stomach cramps, hyper-reactivity and obsessive worrying also decreased from a "10" to a "0." In stressful situations, she was able to easily manage the few symptoms that did appear.

Case 12—An elderly woman with depression came to me with a severe craving for sweets, which she binged on to the detriment of her diabetes. We used TFT to easily reduce her cravings from 10 to 0—and the increased sense of self-control it gave her was also helpful in managing her diabetes. Not only that, but the increased belief in her abilities to lead a healthier life was beneficial in her recovery from depression.

—Caroline E. Sakai PhD

* * *

If simple phobias can be treated with Thought Field Therapy, what about more complex mental disorders? Is the effect on the body's energy pathways and the brain's "emotional filing system" powerful enough to deal with, say, schizophrenia (hearing voices), paranoia, hallucinations or even multiple personality disorder?

Let's take a look at how TFT helped one patient in this story straight from our own patient files.

 ## Quieting the Voices, Relieving the Suffering

Many years ago, I used to specialize in treating schizophrenia· in my private practice in Detroit. My colleagues would often send me their schizophrenics since they did not enjoy working with them and I did. Years ago, I found that TFT and the advanced TFT technique of Voice Technology (VT) could eliminate all traces of paranoia.

More recently, I treated two schizophrenics who had been hospitalized during the severest point in their illness. One suffered from paranoid symptoms and anxiety, yet progressed nicely with TFT. The other was nearly driven to the brink of another complete mental breakdown by intrusive hallucinatory voices.

This second case was the first time I had used TFT for the immediate removal of hallucinatory voices. While there isn't a "standard" TFT sequence for the problem, the correct treatment for this particular patient was revealed by Voice Technology—a method that I and advanced TFT practitioners use to diagnose and develop a custom sequence for clients and patients.

The patient was a young man—just 22 years old. He had been hospitalized and diagnosed as schizophrenic; his hallucinations were severe. He continuously heard voices throughout the day which threatened to drive him back to the hospital. His grandmother, who had been successfully treated by TFT for a quite different problem a number of years ago, pleaded with me to accept him in treatment immediately since he seemed on the verge of cracking up due to the utter despair caused by these voices.

The client, "Richard," told me the voices were ever-present, troubling him at a "9" on the 10-point SUD scale. I used Voice Technology to diagnose him and discovered a number of

---

∗ Schizophrenia is a mental disorder where the patient loses touch with reality, suffers paranoia, and has hallucinogenic episodes—hearing voices and seeing images that aren't there.

disruptions in his thought field and energy pathways. Not only that, but I immediately perceived there were toxins present—substances and scents that were uniquely toxic to him.

After removing the offending substances and correcting for these toxins, we slowly reduced the voices in his head from a "9" to a "7½" to a "5" to a "1." At each stage, my diagnosis revealed that a different TFT sequence was required. At two different stages, a psychological reversal occurred—that is, a reversal or blockage in the body's internal energy flow that interferes with the effectiveness of any therapy or healing.

After correcting for psychological reversal, Richard and I proceeded with further tapping sequences until the hallucinogenic voices were stilled. Though Richard reported they had stopped, I still ran my own tests to insure the results and found no trace of the problem remaining.

In other words, the voices simply weren't there anymore.

Over the past three decades of work to improve and refine Thought Field Therapy, these treatment sequences still have the power to astonish me with their effectiveness in a wide range of instances—including those situations that seem too severe or dire to be helped by any means. TFT...there has never been anything like it.

—Roger J. Callahan, PhD

* * *

Often times, people end up suffering emotional trauma and other psychological disorders for years—either because they fear traditional therapy, don't seek treatment because they don't want to believe they are "mentally ill," or simply have tried conventional therapy with no results.

How long could a person suffer with a debilitating disorder—only to get relief with TFT? Decades, unfortunately, as we learn from this next story about one man who suffered anxiety for more than 60 years.

After 60 Years, Nothing Worked Until TFT

Most conventional therapies are ineffective when compared with TFT. As a result, many people suffer from psychological problems for most of their lives because they never receive effective treatment.

In a fascinating patient case I worked with, a 71-year-old man was cured of a distressing anxiety disorder after 60 years of suffering.

Though I had never met him, "Gerard" made an appointment to see me at Glasgow's Nuffield Hospital after reading an article about my work with TFT in the Scottish *Daily Record* newspaper. He had suffered from an upsetting problem all his life. Every time he looked someone in the eye, he imagined the other person thought he was staring at them. This made him break eye contact and feel anxious. As a result, he was socially inhibited and found it difficult to hold a conversation.

Over the years he had received cognitive behaviour therapy ("talk therapy") and hypnosis but neither of these had helped. He had also tried meditation, but this was equally unsuccessful in lessening his symptoms.

I suspected Gerard might be suffering from a form of obsessive-compulsive disorder (OCD) and quickly made a diagnosis in order to determine a tapping sequence.

Initially, his SUD (*subjective units of distress*) was a "6." But within minutes it had dropped to a "1."

As a precaution—and to prevent a return of his symptoms—I checked him for toxins and discovered corn was a problem for him. I advised him to repeat the tapping sequences if the problem recurred, and avoid eating corn and corn-based products in the meantime.

When I saw Gerard again two weeks later, he walked into my consulting room with a broad smile on his face. He had carefully noted his results over the previous two weeks in writing—and had clearly gotten immediate results.

As he left the hospital, he walked slowly, stopping by the local shopping mall to go through the shops. The people he had asked for directions couldn't have been friendlier, he reported, but more importantly he was relaxed and calm—finally appreciating life after 60 years of turmoil. Later, he went for an enjoyable and invigorating walk with the dog, when previously he would have returned home stressed and tired from such a walk.

Another day, Gerard went out to run errands and ran into a former neighbour. Gerard's approach was open and friendly. He spoke fluently, without stress, feeling wonderful about being his authentic self.

Interestingly, Gerard had no recurrence of his symptoms after his first appointment—probably because he agreed to stay away from corn (a toxin for him). At his second appointment, he no longer tested toxic for corn, so I told him he could eat it every four days.

Gerard's only regret was that he could not have been treated with TFT 60 years ago, as his whole life would have been so much better.

—Dr. Colin Barron

Tapping Away Phobias & Controlling Disorders

You'll find videos that step you through the complete
tapping sequences for phobias and other disorders at our website:

www.rogercallahan.com/pathways

Chapter Six:
Ending Embarrassment

After reading many of the stories in this book, you might believe that TFT is only meant for "real" issues like post-traumatic stress disorder, paralyzing phobias, chronic anxieties, depression and addictions. But what about those everyday people who haven't suffered a traumatic episode or simply don't have "issues" to deal with? Perhaps, like many people, you struggle with far less severe issues on a day-to-day basis.

Embarrassment is one such issue we commonly see.

And whether it's embarrassment about body image, a career or employment situation, a physical trait or habit we've acquired—or any reason—embarrassment can make us reticent in social situations, limit our enjoyment of interactions with others, and keep us from making decisions that might uplevel every aspect of our lives—if only we had the confidence to do so.

Not only can TFT help eliminate the feelings of embarrassment, it can often help erase the underlying issue that gives us cause for embarrassment to begin with. In this first story, about an 81-year-old woman who had lived with embarrassment for years, a local TFT practitioner is able to calm the embarrassment and address her underlying challenge, too.

 When Embarrassment Becomes Extreme

"Mary," an 81-year-old woman I once worked with, said her main problem was that she was overweight—and she was extremely embarrassed about it. Although she listed other challenges, she rated those as having considerably lower impact than her weight issue. In fact, she stated that her SUD (*subjective units of distress*) about her overweight condition was an "8."

This surprised me. From where I sat, Mary did not look extremely overweight to me for a woman of her age, so I suspected that there were a number of other emotions involved.

Knowing that most problems have layers to them, I decided to take a different approach by tackling the emotions behind Mary's perception of her weight problem. As we talked, there were indeed many layers to her weight problem including embarrassment, anger and guilt. Of these, she reported embarrassment as the highest emotion, especially when her children commented on her weight. She reported an initial SUD of 5 with respect to embarrassment. I began to use the TFT diagnostic methods to create a tapping sequence specifically designed to clear the embarrassment. Her SUD went down immediately.

In fact, once we tapped out the treatment, she remarked, "I don't care anymore! I can't think of being embarrassed about my weight."

Mary felt TFT was extremely helpful dealing with her feelings of embarrassment—leaving her feeling more at peace with herself. But we weren't quite finished with our session.

Because she had also stated her distress about her weight was an "8" on the SUD scale of 0 to 10, I used the TFT diagnostic methods to create a tapping sequence specific to her weight problem.

Because weight issues are often related to toxins, I also tested her for toxin interference, and recommended that she stay away from her identified toxins as much as possible. For each toxin identified, I also tested for how many times a day she needed to treat herself with TFT while those toxins were still in her environment. As it turns out, the toxins we identified for her were the specific brands of laundry detergent, dish soap, floor cleaner, and other household products she was using. We also found that some food items were toxic for her.

I taught her how to do the 7-Second Toxin Treatment to help neutralize the toxins until she could purchase dye- and perfume-free cleaning products without the harsh chemicals.

After two weeks, Mary confirmed that she was still feeling good about herself and that the "weight issue" had not bothered her at all. In fact, she said it was like the embarrassment of her weight had never been a problem.

—*Priya Pinto, PhD*

* * *

In today's culture, weight is a major challenge that causes many people embarrassment about their bodies. Even after someone loses significant weight and is trim and healthy again, the old thoughts of "I'm overweight" can present real physical challenges.

In this interesting story of a formerly obese man who lost significant weight, TFT helped reduce the feelings of embarrassment—but also addressed his lack of energy and the emotions we sometimes see with anorexic patients who, while extremely thin, still "see" themselves as obese.

 ## The Mirror Will Tell

A patient of mine, "Jonathan," had had stomach-reduction surgery to address extreme obesity which, by that point, had caused related health issues. The surgery was very successful, he said, in that he had lost an enormous amount of weight, which was clearly visible just in his face. Neither was he disgruntled with the necessary restrictions the surgery had required. Further, he explicitly told me that he was not interested in any therapy treatment to address his body image or any treatment to improve his energy.

In both those areas, he said, he was fine.

However, after a bit of questioning about his new lifestyle, it was apparent that he didn't actually feel any better in terms of increased energy (which would normally be an instant benefit of losing excessive weight)—and more surprising, he thought that there was no improvement in his appearance.

In fact, he typically became angry when someone complimented him on his improved looks.

Having treated several anorexic clients, I was familiar with how intractable such delusions can be. However, I was not troubled by it, recalling that Dr. Callahan once said delusions could be eliminated with TFT diagnostic procedures and custom tapping sequences.

Opting to treat the anger and body image issues at a later session, I worked with him on the more immediate problem of toxins and low energy. He was highly motivated which made toxin elimination very successful.

Finally, by our third session, we were ready to address the delusion around his body image. At the outset, I had an insight to examine him for psychological reversal· in this area.

What gave me the insight? His voice tested weak when he said, "I have lost a lot of weight," but it was extremely strong when he said, "I am as fat as ever."

This psychological reversal was readily corrected.

Next I took Jonathan into the men's room where there was a large mirror. I had him stand in front of it and acknowledge that he had in fact lost weight and looked it. In approximately 30 minutes, I retested the two sentences to make sure the correction held; it did. The following week, his body image was still high as he reported the experience of being complimented by someone and genuinely receiving it graciously—without hostility.

—*Robert Gairing, PhD*

* * *

Poor body image—and the embarrassment it causes—can also arise from physical circumstances other than excessive weight. In this next story about a cancer survivor who underwent reconstructive surgery, her embarrassment risked creating a lifetime of limiting beliefs for her. Take a look...

---

* Psychological reversal (or "PR") is a blockage or reversal of the energy flows in your body's energy pathways. It keeps all kinds of treatments from working as well as they should. PR can be easily eliminated by tapping midway on the outside edge of your hand prior to using other tapping sequences for your illness or disorder. TFT practitioners always test for PR prior to TFT treatment.

"I'll Never Be Attractive to Someone New…"

I once worked with a woman who had undergone a double mastectomy 10 years earlier. Back then, the prosthesis—or substance used for reconstruction of her breast tissue—was not as "natural" as is used today. The result of this was that she felt alienated from her breasts and could not imagine anyone finding her attractive in the nude because of them.

This belief became exacerbated as she was facing a divorce and could not imagine a new partner finding her attractive.

Using TFT diagnostic procedures, I pursued this issue of negative body image—with her enthusiastic cooperation—and within a few minutes we had eliminated the negative feeling associated with her breasts. Of course, the ultimate test would occur that evening when she disrobed prior to retiring for the night.

At our next session, it was so wonderful to hear her tell me that seeing herself that night confirmed that "the feeling" was gone and that her breasts "felt warm."

After 30 years of clinical work, TFT is enabling me to realize a dream that I have had since my doctoral studies in 1974: to be able to heal people quickly and completely with precision and extraordinary efficacy. Thank you, Dr. Callahan, for this marvelous therapy.

—*Robert Gairing, PhD*

* * *

Embarrassment comes in many forms, causes many different responses, and can be caused by an incalculable number of reasons. In this next story, a elderly woman suffers from shame and embarrassment after falling victim to a financial predator.

Financial Scam Causes Shame for This Senior

I call my mother every day. One particular day was different. My 85-year-old mother let slip a comment: "Pretty soon I will be able to take care of all the grandkids in my will." I asked, "What do you mean, Mom?"

"Oh," she said, "I'm not ready to talk about it right now." An alarm went off, and I was like a firefighter heading to a blaze.

My parents are on a small fixed income. They, like most loving grandparents, have spent years bailing out grandchildren, choosing to sacrifice their own needs. I knew how precious little they had. I reminded my mother that I had provided her with an 800 number so her calls to me are always free and asked her to tell me more when she felt ready. Two days later the bombshell exploded: "Hi, this is Mom. Now I feel ready to tell you that I won six million dollars, but I have to send money to some third-world country by Monday in order to claim my prize."

I asked my mother if she felt comfortable sharing the information with me so I could research the authenticity of the award letter. Once I got all the information, I hung up and called the Indianapolis consumer protection and fraud division. They were useless. I then called the local police station where the dispatcher said that it would be helpful if a family member accompanied the police officer to write up a report of fraud. He explained that they had received numerous complaints about a predator scamming seniors out of their hard-earned money. He went on to explain that embarrassment and shame stop many seniors from even reporting the crime.

I contacted my sister Sandy. As a precaution, she called their local bank, only to discover $7,000 had been drawn from my parents' account, and, thankfully, an aware and thoughtful bank employee stopped another $20,000 check from being cashed. This event would not have happened a year ago; it was the first inkling of my parents' decline. I would have to intervene over the next few months, but the emotional trauma associated with the scam lingered on.

What I didn't realize when I first learned of this was how emotionally devastated she was. When we talked on the phone, she cried and expressed how useless, foolish, and ashamed she felt. She made a comment to the effect that everyone would be better off if she wasn't around anymore. She couldn't sleep, and she agonized over the loss of family finances.

I flew to Indiana the following week to see her. "Mom," I said, "How would you feel if we did some Thought Field Therapy to alleviate your distress?"

With her permission, I asked her, "Describe your distress level on a scale from 1 to 10, with 10 being the most distressed." She said it was a definite 10. After we worked together for about ten minutes using the trauma sequence, her distress level dropped to a minimal level, surprising us both! The next day, while sharing lunch, Mom leaned over and said, "I had such a good night's sleep. I can't conjure up any negative emotion around the perpetrator who stole my hard-earned money."

Thankfully, we had introduced a degree of comfort and emotional balance back into her life.

—*Mary Lou Dobbs*

Tapping Away Embarrassment

You'll find videos that step you through the complete tapping sequence for ending embarrassment at our website:

www.rogercallahan.com/pathways

Chapter Seven:
Tackling the Underlying Stress
of Troublesome Disorders

We've talked extensively about how Thought Field Therapy uses the body's energy pathways to promote healing and overall well-being. But if we look a little closer at the ancient science and wisdom behind this phenomenon, it's easy to understand how TFT can so quickly and easily bring about healing and relief.

For over 5,000 years, the Chinese have known that vital life energy flows throughout the body's many energy pathways. When this flow of energy becomes blocked, it can spark disease and other physical ailments. Of course, the Chinese have used acupuncture to effectively clear energy blockages along these pathways. TFT uses tapping to clear emotional blockages and toxic stress along these same pathways.

If you have a troubling disorder, such as insomnia, joint pain, digestive upset, sinus trouble or any other ongoing condition, that's a sign that your vital life energy is out of balance. Stress, anxiety, unreleased trauma, grief or any one of a number of other common and perfectly normal emotions are creating blockages within your energy systems. Unfortunately, not only can these energy pathways cause disease when they are blocked, they are also stopped from doing the restorative and healing work they do every day in an otherwise normally functioning body.

In other words, not only do blockages cause disease, they also prevent recovery. And while modern medicine has developed thousands of drugs to address the symptoms of individual diseases, these medications don't treat the underlying cause of the disease itself.

TFT, on the other hand, can easily unblock these energy flows and bring about rapid and astonishing recovery. In fact, we often see evidence of the early stages of recovery within minutes of administering a TFT treatment.

We've received countless stories from people who got relief of "incurable" diseases with TFT. Turn the page to read just a few.

TFT Cures Insomnia When Nothing Else Will

Insomnia is a common problem which affects up to one-third of the population. Some sufferers get no sleep at all, others require a long time to fall asleep, while still others are troubled with early morning wakening.

I have suffered from occasional insomnia since my late teens. Originally, it only affected me about one night in ten. It gradually worsened over the years until I was plagued with early-morning wakening and poor sleep quality almost every night.

Over the years I had tried all sorts of remedies including homeopathic and herbal preparations, lavender aromatherapy oil, autogenic training and self-hypnosis—nothing worked. In the past few years, as I have trained in neuro-linguistic programming and hypnotherapy, numerous "experts" have attempted to cure me with their favored therapies including regressive hypnosis and "brief therapy" techniques. One hypnotist even suggested that, when I could not sleep, I should get up and read my insurance policies!

All of these therapeutic interventions were totally unsuccessful and when the therapists concerned learned of their failure, they sometimes became angry, often suggesting that I should "just pull myself together and sleep properly." One therapist suggested that I must have a "secondary gain" from my lack of sleep—which is therapist-speak for getting a psychological benefit from a troubling disorder and continuing it purposely in order to get the underlying "benefit"!

Then I met Dr. Roger Callahan while studying as a practitioner in his TFT diagnostic training program. He diagnosed my insomnia and created a simple tapping sequence for me to use before going to bed at night. He also identified several toxins which were affecting my system—namely wheat, milk, garlic, black pepper and yeast.

Within a few days of using the TFT sequence and cutting out the toxins from my diet, my sleep pattern improved dramatically. In fact, I had my first proper night's sleep in months!

And while I've had a few relapses since then, each could be traced to additional toxins I wasn't aware of before such as sugar, artificial sweeteners, cream, honey, cranberries and corn flakes. I also bought new pillows, bought a different mattress cover and changed my laundry detergent.

Though I've had to make radical changes in my diet and can no longer eat many of my favourite foods, I believe the sacrifice is small compared with the benefits of sleeping well at night.

It just goes to show that most of the orthodox treatments for insomnia favoured by doctors are useless and that true insomnia is always caused by toxins. TFT—and the information about toxins that I learned—worked when nothing else did.

—*Dr. Colin Barron*

* * *

Insomnia is only one of many troubling disorders that TFT can help, but the biggest benefit is that TFT carries no side effects—as many drugs prescribed for such conditions do. In this next story about a patient who reacted badly to his gout medication—without receiving any relief of the gout itself—TFT cured his gout and reversed the negative side effects of the drug.

 ## At Wit's End When Gout Lingers Longer

"Matthew" was distraught and pale when he came to see me. He was looking for natural treatments for a severe case of gout which had been ongoing for nearly two months. It had affected the big toe on his right foot with severe redness, swelling, and acute pain and tenderness throughout his foot—requiring him to use crutches for weeks since he was unable to walk and could not wear shoes.

---

* Gout is a common type of arthritis caused by an increased concentration of uric acid in biological fluids. The uric acid crystals are deposited in tendons, joints, kidneys and other tissues where they cause considerable inflammation and damage.

It was undoubtedly one of the worst cases of gout I had seen in my entire medical career.

Matthew's primary doctor had sent him to a rheumatologist who had prescribed Colchicine, an anti-inflammatory drug. Usually over 75% of patients see significant improvement with Colchicine within 12 hours. Yet Matthew's gout did not respond at all to this medication. In fact, the swelling in his toe and foot had actually increased, and his gums were bleeding from the side effects of this medication. Additionally, since he had not responded to the Colchicine, the rheumatologist wanted to start him on another medication, Allopurinol, which also happens to have toxic side effects.

On his own, Matthew had made the necessary changes to his diet—but there was no improvement in his symptoms. Eventually, the underlying cause of his unending gout became clear.

He was under severe stress because his sister had metastatic breast cancer, and other loved ones had passed away the previous month. In addition, due to his physical debilitation and severe pain, he was unable to work—which had caused financial hardship and marital problems as a result.

Before even discussing natural remedies to treat his gout, I used TFT's diagnostic procedures to create a unique treatment sequence for the severe pain of Matthew's gout. Next, I treated his intense anger and frustration that the gout had not improved in over two months and was actually getting worse. As a result of these treatments, his pain, anger and frustration—which was initially at a 10++ on the SUD scale—went to a "1" in just a few minutes.

In addition, I treated him for trauma, depression and anxiety arising from his sister's cancer and from the recent deaths in his life—watching his distress drop from a "10" to a "1" using just the trauma sequence. I also treated him for the stress and anxiety caused by his financial and marital problems, which rapidly decreased from a "10" to a "1."

He was amazed at how rapidly so much stress, trauma and pain could be cleared in just minutes. After the treatments, he actually started smiling and laughing, and his complexion improved.

We then discussed natural remedies for his gout, and I instructed him to continue the collarbone breathing three times a day—asking him to check back with me in a week's time.

To my surprise, two days later he walked into my office without the crutches and without any pain! In addition, the swelling, redness and tenderness were practically gone. He said in the evening following our initial appointment, he noticed the swelling, redness and tenderness starting to diminish. Not only that, but he had visited his Family Doctor and Rheumatologist who were astounded at his tremendous improvement.

—*Roopa Chari, M.D.*

* * *

Foot pain is almost unbearable to live with. It not only limits a person's movement, it can lead to other issues such as loss of work and further injury due to decreased mobility.

In this next story, TFT works on the underlying cause of a mysterious foot ailment that won't go away.

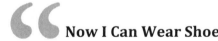

Now I Can Wear Shoes

"How did you do this?" the staff asked grimly at the foot doctor's office. After weeks of treating a mysterious infection and removing portions of what we thought was an ingrown toenail, there were still no signs of improvement.

Eventually, I had an operation to permanently remove the side of the toenail, using self-hypnosis to speed my recovery. While my doctor was impressed by how well the area had healed, the toenail also grew back almost immediately and began to cause problems again. Even worse, the injured toenail had caused hypergranulation· in the area. At the time, I was performing

---

* Also known as "proud flesh," hypergranulation is a red, grainy-looking area of healing at the site of an injury.

in a local opera and I put it down to the uncomfortable shoes I had to wear for a short time each night. (Later, I discovered that the stage make-up I was using had been toxic for me.)

Again more chunks of nail and skin were removed. Talk about painful! But still no lasting improvement was achieved— then another procedure was required to remove more of the offending toenail.

My patient file was getting larger, and clearly the doctor could not understand why.

I knew about TFT and around this same time, I was starting to look at its wider uses. It dawned on me that I could treat the underlying stress and emotions related to the toenail problem. The realization didn't come a moment too soon, because by this time I was unable to wear normal shoes—even though I would soon be leaving for my summer holiday abroad.

While my holiday could be spent in sandals, I knew I had to solve my foot problem by the time cold weather arrived.

I did a short session of TFT and identified no healing blocks (a relief!), but STILL I could not wear shoes. Knowing the power of TFT, this puzzled me.

After returning from my holiday, I wanted to be able to join a gym which meant having to wear athletic shoes. I had an initial training session booked and yet was not able to wear the appropriate footwear. My toe area was still very sore and the old method of soaking it in hot salt water was getting me nowhere.

I came to realize that the discomfort was a sign that there were disturbances in my "thought field." At the very last moment, I called for help from a TFT practitioner trained in advanced techniques. My session took only five minutes, though there were an amazing number of long sequences to tap. I discovered this is common if there are toxins present. Sure enough, we identified and resolved several toxins.

As a result, the pain in my toenail went away instantly and the inflamed area faded to a lighter shade of pink. A calmness spread over me, and off I went to the gym.

Unfortunately, complete relief was still elusive. While the pain and inflammation had lessened considerably, my toe still sometimes felt uncomfortable. Once for instance, when I changed to a different pair of gym shoes, I had to take them off immediately because they hurt after just a minute or two. The next day I confirmed with my TFT practitioner, Dr. Colin Barron, that they were toxic for me. As long as I stayed away from products and clothing items that were "toxic" for me, my toe would remain calm—though not fully healed.

Interestingly, around this time, I also began to do research into how effective TFT might be for eliminating tics. I had a tic* sometimes of repeatedly scratching my head. I used to do it in the car when driving, even though it would dangerously send me into a trance. I decided to identify which toxins were causing this and was very quickly able to identify that wheat was toxin for me.

When I stopped eating wheat products, not only did my tic improve—immediately and dramatically—but also did my TOE!

The mystery had been solved with TFT.

—*Rosemary Wiseman*

* * *

Underlying stress—with the added stress of toxins in our environment—is the cause of many troubling disorders. Nothing could be truer of Irritable Bowel Syndrome, a painful, relentless and restrictive disorder that is widely regarded as being incurable. One TFT practitioner, however, decided to test TFT's effectiveness with this troublesome disorder and achieved amazing results with nearly a dozen clients.

Not "Incurable" After All

With so many clients approaching me for help with Irritable Bowel Syndrome, I decided to conduct a brief survey with 11 individuals—this time using Thought Field Therapy as the test

---

* A tic is either an involuntary spasm or contraction usually of the face, neck or shoulder muscles which often becomes more pronounced under stress—or a behavioural quirk that someone acts out frequently without thinking.

treatment, instead of the many pharmaceutical drugs that are typically used with patients suffering from the disorder.

Not only were the results important in that IBS is widely regarded as an incurable condition, they were important because the few treatments available are directed at simply reducing the severity of its many presenting symptoms rather than curing the disease in its entirety.

Irritable Bowel Syndrome (IBS) is a disorder that appears in multiple forms and with varying symptoms and severity—with an estimated one in four people in the developed world affected at some time in their lives. It is a bowel disorder characterized by abdominal pain, painful defecation, unpredictable and irregular bowel habits, and bloating of the intestines. Other symptoms include nausea, vomiting, fatigue, backache, headache and, in women, gynecological or urological symptoms. Disturbed emotions, notably anxiety states, are also a feature.

Unfortunately, because of a host of various symptoms, a diagnosis of IBS can usually only be reached when all other possible diseases and abnormalities are ruled out. Patients often see multiple doctors as a result—making diagnosis even more difficult and misdiagnosis common. Laparoscopy is regularly performed, with inappropriate surgery such as hysterectomy, cholecystectomy and appendectomy occasionally the consequence of misdiagnosis.

Regarded by many physicians as "non-serious", IBS is nevertheless an extremely common disorder, accounting for up to 50% of all cases seen by gastroenterologists. It is accepted by conventional medical practitioners that any treatment they can offer is of little proven benefit, yet a large number of sufferers endure many months or years of invasive investigations and treatment procedures in the hope that some relief from the condition may be obtained.

Hoping to find a long-term non-invasive solution, I assembled a client group from amongst my practice comprised of 9 women and 2 men, ranging in age from 27 to 48 years. Each had suffered from IBS anywhere from 3 to 14 years. All had initially sought treatment from their respective general practitioners and had undergone many investigative procedures to exclude other diseases. All had also been prescribed anti-spasmodics to control their symptoms, but described the impact of the medication as insignificant.

Needless to say, they were all considerably anxious and depressed about their condition.

With each client, I initially used TFT's *psychological reversal* technique to uncover what the client felt was most distressing in their life—from Trauma and General Stress, to Obsession, Shame, Embarrassment, Guilt, and so on. I followed with a diagnostic session and unique tapping sequence just for them if no significant reduction in SUD (*subjective units of distress*) were reported. Once the client reported a SUD of 2 or 1, the treatment was regarded as complete. I didn't offer a treatment for the physical pain that often accompanies IBS because I wanted to see if this symptom disappeared as a consequence of the initial TFT treatment.

During the treatments, I made two main observations:

- All subjects tested strong for psychological reversal with six requiring special breathing procedures to overcome it.
- All tested strong for at least three toxins, though no common pattern emerged whether the toxins were wheat, corn, milk, chocolate, cola, or other products. However, craving for the individually identified toxins was confirmed by the client after testing.

The subjects were provided with self-help instructions for the custom tapping sequences, and were instructed to carry out treatments 20 times a day. A follow-up appointment was scheduled one week later, then four weeks later.

What were the results?

- Four of the subjects saw their IBS condition completely resolve. These four confirmed they had followed my instructions exactly, including checking for toxins not

---

* Psychological reversal (or "PR") is a blockage or reversal of the energy flows in your body's energy pathways. It keeps all kinds of treatments from working as well as they should. PR can be easily eliminated by tapping midway on the outside edge of your hand prior to using other tapping sequences for your illness or disorder. TFT practitioners always test for PR prior to TFT treatment.

identified during treatment and eliminating their intake of the newly identified toxins.

- Five reported partial resolution with considerable reduction in the number and severity of their emotional and gastrointestinal symptoms. Three of these five admitted they had not done the tapping procedure at home as often as advised, but had made attempts to track accurately, yet not fully.

- Two reported no change whatsoever in their IBS condition. They did, however, admit to a secondary gain· from their problem and so had stopped treatment when it was realized that their symptoms were resolving.

We know that most people who have chronic IBS also have heightened emotions such as anxiety, depression, phobias, and hostility. We also know that IBS is recognized as a "disorder of intestinal motility"—a condition in which the intestine's normal contractions become abnormal, leading to spasms and even intestinal paralysis such that digesting food simply does not pass through the intestines properly.

Since intestinal motility is under the control of the autonomic nervous system—that part of the brain which controls involuntary body functions like breathing, reflexes and digestion—I believe TFT succeeds in eliminating IBS because of its ability to rebalance the autonomic nervous system.

In other words, when normal autonomic nervous function is returned, intestinal motility also returns to normal with other symptoms resolving soon afterward.

—Ian Graham

* * *

While the previous story tells us that toxins, stress and other outside factors can bring about the onset of troubling disorders,

---

* Subject 1 declined further treatment despite improvement as she would lose her Disability Living Allowance if she recovered. Subject 2 declined further treatment despite improvement as recovery would mean she would be obliged to resume sexual relations with her husband.

millions of people are born with disorders or genetic defects that require constant medication or other treatment so the patient can function normally. Does TFT help with these disorders?

Yes!

In this next story about a TFT practitioner who suffers *primary immune disease*—a genetic defect—we learn that TFT helps him manage the disorder and overcome the discomfort of ongoing, life-long treatments.

Thousands of Antibodies, Hours of Pain

When I completed the TFT practitioner's training, I made a conscious decision that—in order to best prepare myself as a TFT therapist—I should probably use and experience TFT in my own healing process.

I have *primary immune deficiency disease*—a disorder in which part of the body's immune system is missing or does not function properly. In contrast to *secondary* immune deficiency disease (in which the immune system is compromised by outside factors such as viruses or chemotherapy), primary immune deficiency disease is caused by inherent or genetic defects in the immune system.

Like me, many individuals affected by primary immune deficiency disease require lifelong therapy including intravenous gamma globulin infusions, antibiotic therapies, or bone marrow transplants.

Since 1985 when I was first diagnosed with the condition, I've received monthly Gamma globulin infusions where thousands of antibodies are infused into my body.

Unfortunately, I eventually began to experience pain in my lower back, stomach, and chest during the infusion treatments. To prepare for an upcoming infusion, I used a unique TFT sequence given to me by Dr. Roger Callahan, and I also used the TFT toxin treatment for the Gamma globulin I was about to receive.

I did these treatments three times the evening prior to the infusion and three times the morning of the infusion. About an hour into the infusion I began to experience pain in my lower back, stomach, and chest. Most of the pain was in my lower back—about a "7" on the SUD scale of 0 to 10.

Using one hand, I did the two TFT treatments I had previously done that morning and the pain immediately decreased to a "3." After repeating the two treatments again, the pain faded to a "1" and remained there until the end of the infusion. At the end of the infusion, I felt much better than I had during previous Gamma globulin sessions.

For the next two months, I tapped out the TFT sequences before and during my infusion treatments. Within 90 days of starting to use TFT with my monthly treatments, I was able to go through an entire infusion without feeling any discomfort. I think it's made a significant difference in my being able to experience the infusion without side effects.

Not only that, but I meet with my doctor after every infusion. He had in his notes to begin me on antibiotics for the winter, but because I'm doing so well he decided to hold off on prescribing them. This is a huge benefit, because I want antibiotics to be effective for me whenever I do need them (routine antibiotic use weakens their effectiveness over time).

I've been very fortunate for the past 20 years to have a life saving treatment available—the infusion of Gamma globulin which gives me the gift of antibodies from thousands of individuals. Now I feel that I've been given a second life-saving gift…Thought Field Therapy.

—*Tom McDermott*

* * *

Since TFT rebalances the body's internal energy pathways, it can help all kinds of health problems that arise within this interconnected energy field. While Thought Field Therapy is not a substitute for emergency medical treatment, it can significantly ease situations where emergency treatment has been necessary or where ongoing treatment for chronic disease is needed.

Calming the "Perfect Storm" of Medical Events

As we approached the runway from what seemed a never-ending flight, my husband suffered a heart attack. He had started dialysis the year before after being diagnosed with *polycystic kidney disease*—a condition which had already caused the deaths of both his father and his brother.

Now, it seemed history might repeat itself.

While dialysis provided numerous health benefits, we learned that polycystic disease and dialysis can also contribute to a number of other health problems.

Dangerously low blood pressure is one of them. And it was the culprit on that fateful day as we were landing at the airport. Fortunately, airport medics were able to be on the scene very quickly. Additionally, I had started treating him immediately with TFT, so the heart attack did the least damage that it possibly could have. Also, my husband said he never felt the horrible gripping pain that others have said accompanies heart attacks.

Within minutes of arriving at the hospital, he was in emergency surgery so doctors could insert a stent into one of his arteries.

Several weeks after the stent was put in, however, he began to have chest pains when he walked. No one told us that stents could close off, but I should have known that a serious problem existed because—when we used Thought Field Therapy during his recovery period—we had difficulty maintaining normalcy in his condition.

His cardiologist ordered another surgery since it appeared the stented artery had almost entirely closed off, with only a trickle of blood getting through.

The medications that my husband needed to take as a result of the heart attack also caused problems. The blood thinner caused him to get "bleeders"—spontaneous spots with bleeding that were difficult to control. We found that by touching the spot and tapping on the side of the hand—and sometimes using some of the other TFT treatments—we were able to quickly stop the bleeding.

Not only that but the stent that doctors inserted during his second surgery was toxic to his system, as it contained medication that was continually releasing into his body. We treated him numerous times for that specific toxicity until it no longer tested toxic for him.

Of course, all of his heart problems aside, my husband was still undergoing regular dialysis treatments. Soon, he was having breathing problems. He would wake up at night unable to take a deep breath. While his dialysis nurse had tested his lungs and said that they were fine, we used the TFT diagnostic procedures to identify toxins that were causing the problem. One such toxin was the over-the-counter medicine he had been asked to take, as well as the soap that he was using.

At home, we use chemical-free laundry detergent, but one weekend when we were out of town, we discovered that the sheets on the bed in the hotel were toxic to him. The detergent in which they were washed must have been toxic. At various points in time, when we would eat out, something in the food would cause him not to be able to breathe properly. Tapping the side of the hand, the outside of the thumb, and the gamut spot were very helpful with the breathing problems, along with other TFT treatments.

Meanwhile, he had started having nightmares of being under water and not being able to get his breath. He also developed a fear of lying down to go to sleep. Using TFT, we treated the nightmares and the fear of lying down so that now, he is sleeping just fine. Interestingly, in the materials we received upon starting dialysis, it says that depression is a common side effect of being on dialysis. TFT had been a powerful treatment for the numerous ups and downs that have occurred since he went on dialysis.

—Jenny Edwards

* * *

If TFT can calm the "perfect storm" of medical events for the husband and dialysis patient above, imagine its effectiveness in bringing about positive changes in an otherwise healthy patient.

Over the last couple of years, we've offered a new course that not only teaches TFT's highest level of effectiveness—Voice Technology—it also focuses on bringing about vibrant good health and positive mental states in addition to healing the emotional and physical ailments our bodies sustain. We call it the Optimal Health program because we address the whole person: mind, body and spirit. Held for the first time in London in 2008, we were excited to begin sharing Voice Technology with more people around the world and see our expanded vision of world healing come to pass.

Since Roger first discovered and developed TFT Voice Technology over 25 years ago, we have seen so many life-changing results. Our trained VT practitioners have also experienced similar amazing healings over the years. Now, as we'll see in this next story, our Optimal Health attendees have learned to achieve significant life-enhancing results from the techniques they learn in the program.

 ## "Dear Roger and Joanne... I'm Pregnant!"

I remember the day Michelle Smith walked into our TFT Optimal Health program. She wanted to start a family, but couldn't. She'd been diagnosed with severe and "incurable" endometriosis which prevented her from becoming pregnant. As a motivated and vivacious young woman, she stepped up as our first volunteer for a demonstration during the class.

Her case exemplifies the healing power of TFT Voice Technology. And in notes to us since the training, she's shared her story of more than a year and a half of using TFT to improve so many aspects of her health and well-being. No one but Michelle—in her own words, as she sent letters and emails to us—could accurately convey her feelings and experience. It's just one more heart-warming story of healing with TFT.

Letter following the Optimal Health program...

"During the class, Roger found my womb and reproductive area to be in psychological reversal· and diagnosed a treatment for the endometriosis which I applied several times that day—as well as repeatedly checking the reproductive area for reversals.

My endometriosis is extremely interesting to treat. It's only mid-cycle, but I treat it every day and when I treat it, it feels like elastic bands snapping inside me on the laparoscopy scars I have near my ovaries—which can be quite painful but only for a second.

There is no known cause or cure for endometriosis so this will be amazing if it works. I will keep you informed. Every month, I suffer from sickness and diarrhea and excruciating pains that make me scream into a towel so as not to scare my husband. I cannot stand up or eat or sleep, and I have been unable to work due to this. Because we are trying for children, I can't have a laparoscopy even if I was willing to, as it means we cannot try for children for six months afterward. My husband is 47 and I am 36, so time is not on our side."

Update a few days later...

"I am currently treating my endometriosis every day and every day I identify new sequences that are needed, sometimes several. I am doing everything I can to avoid toxins and am treating with the toxin treatment those that I miss or discover too late.

The strangest thing was, when I first diagnosed a sequence the first few treatments resulted in my feeling sensations akin to elastic bands snapping inside me—sharp stinging pains that went away in seconds. I also experienced pains around the womb area and on my laparoscopy scars and in my sigmoid area. This happened for the first few days of treatment, but now the treatments are pain free.

＊ Psychological reversal (or "PR") is a blockage or reversal of the energy flows in your body's energy pathways. It keeps all kinds of treatments from working as well as they should. PR can be easily eliminated by tapping midway on the outside edge of your hand prior to using other tapping sequences for your illness or disorder. TFT practitioners always test for PR prior to TFT treatment.

I have yet to experience my endometriosis days, so I am not sure of the outcome yet. I will keep you informed. I am scared to get my hopes up as there is no known cause or cure, so this is my last hope. But at least I have some hope now which I didn't have before!"

Then, we received the following e-mail from Michelle...

"I never thought I would be writing this email two days after telling you I was having problems conceiving due to my endometriosis.

But I discovered yesterday morning that I am pregnant.

Even more shocking is that I conceived the evening of the first Voice Technology training day when Roger treated the endometriosis and womb area for reversals and I spent the rest of the day treating it regularly. I think it's only right and proper to advise you that I think your husband made me fall pregnant!!

What's even more fascinating is that I had no idea. Since the training, I had been avoiding toxins or eliminating them as soon as they appeared, so I had been feeling really well until yesterday.

We invited the parents over to share the good news and we had dinner together, but I didn't have time to be host and test for all the ingredients in the meal. I started to feel very nauseous and faint, so I tested the dinner and found I was toxic to cauliflower so I treated that.

I also treated the nausea and within 15 minutes I felt great again. I am so thrilled that I am entering such an exciting stage in my life, with such amazing tools to make it even more perfect. I promise that if [the baby is born] breach, I will videotape the birth and try tapping the PR spot or any other treatment and send you a copy.

Also, when I took the pregnancy test, it came from an old box and I wasn't sure the result was accurate—so I asked my body the question and Voice Technology told me I was pregnant. When we bought another test, it confirmed the same thing.

I AM PREGNANT!

P.S. This is a secret for now, so please don't tell anyone yet. I need to let my family know first. When everyone knows, you can do what ever you like with this email. I want the world to know!

Thank you for giving me so much hope when no one in the medical world could."

As Michelle's pregnancy progressed, she wrote to say...

I test the pregnancy and baby every day, and everything is great. There were some psychological reversals in the early stages about once a month, but I treated them immediately. In fact, the baby seems to be two weeks ahead for her age. She is definitely no older. That I can guarantee. But she is doing all the things an older baby would do, even though she shouldn't have reached that stage yet. The doctor says she is the size of a baby a bit older, too. So my question is: Is it quite normal for the baby not only to be bigger (which I know can happen), but to be ahead in its development whilst in the womb? I wondered if correcting reversals could make any difference?

I am completely fascinated by the whole process and loving every second—even the indigestion and other more unpleasant side effects which VT has cleared up, too. "Baby brain" (forgetfulness and absentmindedness) makes me forget to use VT occasionally, but eventually I remember to use it and the indigestion clears in 20 minutes, even after having it for 2 days.

And might I just add that some side effects will have doctors telling you that they will only disappear once the baby is delivered (in another five months!). VT totally eliminated these symptoms immediately and the physical problem in three days. No medicines!"

At the 6-month mark, Michelle wrote us this update...

"Just an update, the baby is now three-and-a-half weeks bigger than she is supposed to be—conception dates guaranteed. She is blooming! I have a feeling that VT will have a lot to answer for on Delivery Day, and also have a feeling the pain algorithm is going to come in handy!

When I first learned VT, I started to keep a list of all my toxins and non-toxins, comparing them to the lists I had already had diagnosed before by other VT practitioners. They were all the same, and I found many new ones.

After six months of pregnancy, six months off from Endometriosis, 37 traumas treated and listed in my diary, and using VT treatments daily, I am no longer toxic to dairy.

[In a recent note,] Roger explained that I had become healthier and stronger—I imagine due to having six months off from my illness, which has given my body a chance to recover its full strength. I also refuse to use any chemicals in the house and my husband applies the bleach or any other necessary products when I am not there.

I have discovered that I am toxic to my maternity clothes as they are synthetic to enable them to stretch. Cotton maternity clothes are not easy to come by in the winter. I removed and [used the 7-Second Toxin Treatment] for my toxic trousers and my fidgety legs relaxed almost instantly.

I must confess to walking around in long men's t-shirts most days to give my body a break. Yeast and sugar are a real problem, but I am trying to stay off them and it's like coming off a drug. I have to use the urge tapping sequence to keep me sane and the anger sequence to calm me down. It's ridiculous, but if it means I might get some kind of life back, it's worth the effort.

Sometimes when the baby is jumping around and seems particularly fidgety, I check for toxins and when treated, she settles down. I don't move anywhere, I just treat her whilst lying still. I realize that she always appears active to different degrees about 10 minutes after I eat. Her activity levels increase when I have a toxin. I didn't realize until I saw how much she calmed after TFT treatment."

And in one of the most joyful messages we've ever received:

"Please find a picture of our long awaited VT baby... Olivia Louise. She was born by C-section on 29th May. She weighed in at 8 lbs 15 ozs. I used lots of VT, as I lost a liter of blood in a post-partum hemorrhage, but have not had to use much pain relief at all which got all the midwives talking—especially the first night after the operation.

Will write the full story when I am feeling better, I just wanted to show my beautiful girl off to the world, as I am so very proud and totally in love with her. Kindest regards, Michelle."

Michelle also used TFT in the early months after the birth...

"Apparently they do not know what causes colic in babies, though there are some theories. They know what happens, but not why. They also do not have any cures. TFT works great! It stops the crying very quickly. We also treat psychological reversals on [the baby's] tummy area.

Sometimes the pain algorithm is enough. I tap the side of her hand several times a day and under the nose. Sometimes when she won't sleep and just cries, tapping on the side of her hand is just enough to send her off and stop her fussing. She always giggles when I tap under her nose. TFT is a game to her.

I have included a picture so you can see how well Olivia-Louise is growing. She is 12 weeks old now."

And she continues to use TFT to stay healthy and joyous...

"I thought I would list a few times I have used TFT with my baby. I used VT throughout my pregnancy and treated all the baby's reversals.

Olivia Louise is in the 91st percentile—and in clothes, three months bigger. She isn't chubby; in fact, she is quite lean for a baby. She is just tall and we are a short or average family! Maybe reversals stop us all from growing to our full potential inside the womb and out? Our health advisor says she is intelligent and ahead for her age in language, too.

I have recently used TFT for weaning her off the pacifier which I was told would take a few days, maybe a week. It took two attempts. I would lay her on my legs when she was crying and treat her when she cried for the pacifier. I also used it for myself as it was so upsetting to see her cry.

I also used VT when she recently had a cold. She was very congested to the point of being sick a couple of times. After treating her, the congestion was 70% improved by the next morning.

I have also used VT when I had to give her some medication. I held her on my lap and gave a surrogate toxin treatment. She was able to go to sleep very quickly after that, whereas a few minutes earlier she had been crying hysterically.

Finally, I use TFT whenever she cries, first to eliminate her discomfort and then to discover the cause.

I have also treated myself for tiredness which has been a lifesaver at times—and for my temper because, even if you are a saint, getting up 15 times a night will test anyone's patience. I have felt a bit crazy at times and treating it has changed the way I respond to Olivia.

She is so contented. Everyone says how happy she is. I tap reversals on her hand and under her nose everyday, and she sits on my lap while I do a breathing exercise every morning.

At her eight-month check up, they commented on how she turns the pages of a book and that they do not check for that ability until babies are two years old.

For all those Mums and Dads out there, there is so much opportunity to use TFT with your children. It has made me a much better Mother and we are both so much happier.

Kindest regards and eternal thanks to you, Roger. You have touched so many lives among my family and friends and made such a difference I cannot begin to explain. You deserve a knighthood, for you are an unsung hero."

Michelle has been so inspired by the benefits of TFT—both throughout her pregnancy and as she cares for her baby daughter—that she is working on a book about TFT and motherhood. She welcomes interesting and informative cases and stories.

—*Joanne Callahan*

* * *

Stories like Michelle's aren't the only cases we see of life-changing results with TFT. In this next story, Thought Field Therapy gives a client back his livelihood, after he regains partial vision lost to illness.

On the Road Again

Twenty years ago I worked as a junior ophthalmologist at Glasgow Eye Infirmary. For this reason I have always been interested in using TFT to treat eye conditions.

Of course, it has been known for some years that TFT (particularly VT) can sharpen visual acuity. This should be no surprise—bearing in mind the theories of New York ophthalmologist Dr. William Bates (1860-1931) who, in his classic 1920 text "Perfect Sight Without Glasses," proposed that refractive errors of the eye could be improved or even eliminated by a series of ocular exercises.

Bates believed that refractive errors were largely caused by excessive tension in the extra-ocular muscles. He also discovered a link between the mind and vision, and found that the refractive capability of the eye changes when we tell a lie or even just say an untruth, such as "the sky is green."

It is therefore likely that TFT improves visual acuity by relaxing the extra-ocular muscles.

I've treated two eye cases successfully with TFT's Voice Technology. The first case was a 54-year-old truck driver who had lost his HGV (Heavy Goods Vehicle) license after his vision deteriorated in one eye following optic neuritis (inflammation of the optic nerve) caused by Multiple Sclerosis. In Britain, car drivers are only required to read a number plate (license plate) at 25 yards in order to satisfy the legal requirements on vision for drivers. Poor vision in one eye or (even a missing eye) would not matter. However HGV drivers must have an adequate level of vision in either eye.

Visual acuity is usually measured using a Snellens chart—featuring a series of printed letters of different sizes. Unfortunately I didn't have the ability to test by reading the chart, as I was treating this patient at a distance by telephone. I therefore had to rely on SUD (*subjective units of distress*) ratings—a scale of 0 to 10 which measures the patient's own assessment of the severity of the problem. At the beginning of our first session, my patient assessed his visual acuity as being a "7" on a "10" point scale. I also diagnosed some toxins namely wheat, eggs, chocolate and red wine. By the third session, his vision had improved to a "4" and this improvement did last.

A few weeks later, I received a phone call from the patient who called to say that his vision had improved sufficiently for him to pass his medical test, and have his HGV license reinstated. As well as an improved sharpness of vision, he reported that his color vision was better.

I believe the improvement in this case was due not only to changes in refractive error, but also due to the healing effects of TFT on the optic nerve.

The second eye case I treated recently was a contact lens wearer who suffered from recurring styes, conjunctivitis ("pink eye") and corneal ulcers. Though these conditions were treated with conventional medication by an ophthalmologist, this patient still suffered considerable eye pain. I was able to remove this totally using TFT, and the results usually lasted for a day or two.

Then, one day, a very interesting thing happened.

My patient went to the eye clinic and was told his corneal ulcer had healed. The next morning when he awoke, he realized his eye was red and sore again. He phoned me for a TFT session and I discovered that he had drunk some beer the previous night. This beer was a toxin for him as he was sensitive to wheat. This case is very interesting because it shows that orthodox medical treatments—as well as TFT treatments—can be undone by toxins.

—*Dr. Colin Barron*

* * *

As the following story proves, we don't realize how much we use our eyes until a problem arises that causes impaired vision or even momentary loss of vision.

In this interesting story of an uncommon eye disorder, established medical solutions caused even more problems for this patient than the disorder itself.

For Better or Worse, Life Can Change In a Blink

"It's incurable," doctors told me, as I realized I might have to live with this ridiculous disease forever. Like something from a bad movie, they diagnosed me with *Blepharospasm*—a neurological disorder which is a form of *dystonia* or sustained muscle contractions. The symptoms at the time, which specialists assured me would get progressively worse, were spontaneous eye closure—which doesn't sound like much, but in effect leaves one blind for minutes at a time.

The only treatment available was antispasmodic tablets, antidepressants and Botox injections in the eyelids.

Now, I know to some people the opportunity of having Botox treatments for free sounds like a good one. But trust me. I have been injected at three different hospitals and the results can be quite alarming. Nobody warns you that Botox can, and frequently does, migrate beyond the injection site. The side effects ranged from not being able to close my eyes fully at night to not being able to open them enough to see during the day—to not being able to eat or speak properly, because the Botox had drifted down my face and I was semi-paralyzed for two months.

After 18 months of this horror, I decided to stop the injections and medication as neither were having a positive effect. On top of everything else, I had now developed a slight clenching of the jaw and a nodding of the head—very attractive!

The future was starting to look fairly challenging. We live in the country; no public transport, no village shop. I was just establishing myself as a Life Coach and NLP Master Practitioner, but not only was I sending clients to sleep because of my eye closure, I was also missing all the body language. Each session became more tiring, and it soon became clear that I would have to give up my livelihood. Even if we moved into town, would life be any easier?

It looked unlikely, and negotiating a busy pavement or shop was exhausting.

By now I was finding even socializing with close friends a strain. One doesn't realize how much information is gained visually—a look, a raised eyebrow, body language in general, even lip-reading to a small degree in noisy surroundings.

I could feel myself becoming more and more isolated.

Near the beginning of my illness, I had been introduced to TFT by Paul McKenna when I assisted at one of his trainings. I had subsequently completed the basic TFT practitioner's course and was eager to study more. At that point, I had no idea what was still to come in my life—nor that the following year the Callahans would return to Europe where I could complete my training.

My life was getting more and more limited. I could still read and cook. But not much more. My husband, who was worried and depressed about our future and felt trapped in his job, talked about how we could adapt to our new way of life and perhaps make a new start someplace else. Sadly, we never got to make those plans. After months of depression and six weeks on Prozac, he hung himself in the garage.

That winter was difficult for my sons and me. My older son reluctantly returned to University, but the younger one had already decided not to go. He stayed at home, took a job at the local cinema in the evenings and became my driver and companion during the day. The Blepharospasm prevented me from being able to watch television—something to do with the frequency I think—and although I resisted all offers of medication, I admit to finding solace in the odd bottle of wine. Fortunately it didn't take too many months to realize that the more I drank, the more I cried—and the more I cried, the more I drank!

Although I didn't know it at the time, our luck was about to change when I received the news that the Callahans were due to conduct another practitioners course in Dublin. Though I could hardly get around by myself, I booked without hesitation and trusted that something would turn up. Incredibly, just two weeks before I was to fly to Ireland, I met someone who was on her way home to Dublin. She immediately offered to collect me from the airport, and generally keep an eye on me during my four-day stay in Ireland. Although I was making every effort to retain some of my independence, without her help I would have been exhausted by the journey and might well have missed some of the lectures.

If I am to be honest, I was in no state to understand the course, but I did get the chance to work with Bob Bray who, through TFT, managed to make me feel remarkably better about the loss of my husband and my huge fear of our future—both financially and in practical terms.

I returned to the UK with a new strength, determined that life was not going to get the better of me. I decided to run a Bed and Breakfast from home and set about organizing local advertising and a website. It wasn't long before we had a reasonably good flow of visitors and a fairly steady income, although lower than we needed.

Another year passed and we were all settling into our new life. The boys were taking on new responsibilities at home. It was a learning curve for all of us as we seemed to lurch from one household drama to another. We all understand the idiosyncrasies of the lawnmower now, where the fuses are, how to turn the water off in an emergency, which appliances can set off the trip switch and how to reset the boiler.

Several months later, the Callahans returned to the UK. Again, I lost no time in booking a place—thinking I would pick up all the information that had gone over my head at the previous training. My eyes were in a pretty bad way, but I had learned to adapt as much as possible, although still found the condition exhausting. Towards the end of the course, Roger kindly stepped in and offered to treat me. I was overwhelmed and still remember the train journey home with a feeling of anticipation and immense gratitude—somewhere inside I knew that life was really going to change for the better.

Roger and I worked together, eliminating toxins and dealing with the stress. I had learned a great deal from Joanne about sourcing chemical-free products and set about replacing everything in the house. I changed my diet and introduced Waiora drops.

Guess what!

Within four months, not only I could see, but I could drive and had the ability to consider working from home again as a therapist. I cannot tell you all what a huge relief this physical change had on our lives. My sons had clearly been worried about "what to do with Mum." I celebrated with my first real drive (in Italy). We were on holiday with friends and I offered to drive down the mountain, in the dark, in a left-hand drive car on a road I had never encountered. The boys were unusually silent until we reached the bottom, where we all laughed and cried at the change of events.

I have not looked back and thanks to Roger, Joanne and TFT, I have been saved from the effects of the most debilitating and depressing illness.

—Amanda Moser

* * *

After TFT, Amanda's severe eye condition—which doctors initially told her was progressive and incurable—no longer limited her movement. With TFT, she began to recover and rebuild her life.

But what about other troubling conditions that limit people's lives? In this next story about a heart patient whose doctors have given up on further treatment, TFT helps him manage his disorder and become active again.

Existing Day by Day in Pain and Exhaustion

I was a very active senior—jogging and working out at the gym every day until I started getting short of breath and became more tired. When I went to the doctors, they couldn't believe I was still alive, let alone still exercising. As it turns out, my heart was barely getting any blood. At the age of 68, I had quintuple bypass surgery.

For four hours, doctors worked on my heart which was actually outside of my body for the duration of the surgery. After four days of recovery, while prepping me to go home, they discovered I had a serious erratic heart beat—a condition that forced me to stay in the hospital for 10 more days as doctors tried one combination of drugs after another to control the problem.

Not surprisingly, I was allergic to most of the medicines they tried, so I was a wreck mentally, physically and exhaustion-wise. Regardless, they sent me home to recover and continue the use of blood thinners and various heart medicines to somewhat control the arrhythmia.

After a couple of months, doctors convinced me to have the MAZE procedure done—a procedure performed on the heart's nerves that involves burning the nerve endings to stop the arrhythmia. I did this twice, to no avail. It didn't reduce any irregularity—in fact, I felt even worse.

So I lived on medicine and existed day-to-day in pain, confusion and exhaustion. After coming home from each procedure, I would log in a book—several times a day—my blood pressure and pulse reading so I could monitor my heart.

Eventually, I had to have back surgery, and during the operation, they lost me twice on the operating table. My heart sped up so much that it stopped beating all together. This surgery made the arrhythmia all the worse.

I was told that everything had been done to my heart that could be done, and I would just have to live with it the best way I could.

My daughter questioned the cardiologist about the combination of medicine and wondered if that could be causing my dizziness and shortness of breath. "It doesn't matter," he replied. This, apparently, was my only choice.

Thinking I had no options, I attended a TFT Boot Camp given by Joanne Callahan where I learned a series of tapping sequences to help control pain—since pain is a major trigger for the arrhythmia. I learned the dangers of anesthesia as a major toxin to the body—and discovered how long it can linger in the body. (Doctors had told me that I shouldn't have anesthesia in the future because it affects my heart.) I also discovered from Joanne how certain foods can be toxic to an individual's body, and learned how to test myself to determine what I *can* ingest so it's not toxic for me.

After all this, I found a combination that works for me to control the atrial fibrillation:

1. Get rest when feeling stressed or tired.
2. Drink enough water and stay hydrated.
3. Keep pain levels low by tapping out the TFT sequence for pain.
4. Get myself tested for everything I come into contact with or ingest such as beverages, food, anything that touches my skin—even things like toothpaste, laundry detergent and deodorant.

I now get tested for all colognes, creams, lotions, shampoos, foods and drinks of any type. I stay away from anything containing wheat or corn—including their derivatives. Blueberries, strawberries, cantaloupe, and some apples are toxic for me. Most beers give me a major arrhythmia, however, there are a couple I can drink. I like to work outside, so when I encounter certain weeds, grasses or fragrances which bother me, I perform the 7-Second Toxin Treatment which helps desensitize me to those items.

It's interesting and amazing to me that, if I stay away from those things I have identified as toxic or sensitive, my heart rate stays rock solid in performance. I have gone completely off the heart medicines and at this time take only a blood thinner—which I'll be discontinuing soon in favor of a more natural product called Nattokinase.

If I do something I shouldn't, I know it immediately because I can feel my heart shivering—tripling its rate, then stopping for a couple of beats. When it's acting up, it takes my breath away and I have to lay down or sit quietly until I recover.

Five years later, I'm still logging in my journal my blood pressure and pulse and have physical proof that my heart is in a healthier state because of the training I received in TFT. Thank you, Roger and Joanne, for this wonderful technique that's enabled me to live a healthier, happier life.

—*Dale Solarz*

* * *

We see so many stories of health problems that are helped with TFT, even when conventional medicine has "given up" on the patient. Perhaps the most interesting are case studies of people whom medical tests say are perfectly healthy, yet they still have a troubling disorder that limits their lives—and livelihood. In this next story, we meet three individuals who suffered from dizziness—a condition that is easily treated with TFT.

 ## It's Nice When the World Stops Spinning

How interesting it is to find problems which are not alleviated by conventional treatment, but which can be helped by TFT. Three different patients suffering from dizziness presented me with such an opportunity. While they all had additional complaints, I was intrigued by their troubling dizziness. All were understandably disturbed about it and were fearful of having another episode, and generally would get discouraged after a dizzy spell.

Medical intervention had not been helpful.

One sufferer, a 29-year-old man, was referred to my office for generalized anxiety. In our initial interview, he told me that increased and conflicting work pressures had set off his anxiety. He had also been having daily dizzy spells for the past six weeks. Previous therapy had helped him clarify and better resolve his employment difficulties. However, he was distressed about the continuing dizziness—especially since he frequently drove with his job. A neurological exam and electroencephalogram were normal, however, TFT diagnostic procedures revealed a massive psychological reversal that prevented him from getting well. After a customized tapping sequence for his dizziness, he was symptom-free at his six-week follow-up—and most grateful for the relief.

Another patient, a 37-year-old man first met with me four months after being in a severe car accident where he experienced a loss of consciousness, concussion, subdural hematoma, and herniated cervical disc. My evaluation indicated he was suffering a Post Traumatic Stress Disorder and Post Concussion Syndrome.

By this time, he had very disturbing dizzy spells when laying down and when trying to get up from having had laid down.

The symptoms were so distressing that for the previous few months he had been sleeping in a recliner so as to avoid the dizziness he experienced when laying down. He had these dizzy spells almost 100% of the time when laying down or when getting up after laying down. Since the patient generally did not have dizziness at other times, I asked him to lay down on the floor and to experience his dizziness.

While he was laying down on the office floor, he instantaneously became dizzy. I then used TFT, tapping out a specific sequence for his condition. He instantly felt an abatement of his dizziness, and did not get such symptoms when he arose from the floor. Ten weeks later, he reports no dizzy spells and is now able to sleep in his bed.

A further challenge was presented when a physician referred a 49-year-old Hispanic man who suffers from generalized anxiety and positional dizziness that interfered with his work as a carpenter. TFT had previously helped him with anxiety, even though he speaks very little English and needed translation from his brother. This time, however, he came without his brother. By combining my limited Spanish vocabulary with his limited English skills, we were able to get through a treatment and his dizziness was cured using TFT. Not only that, but he was symptom-free when I saw him for a follow-up visit 11 weeks later.

Besides being useful in treating dizziness, TFT has also been helpful in such non-conventional areas as reducing pain, reducing the emotional disturbance associated with chronic pain and illness, reducing the severity and disturbance of tinnitus, and facilitating a fuller and faster recovery from Post Concussion Syndrome.

With TFT, a therapist can save a patient unnecessary suffering and dependency on unwanted medication by addressing instead the underlying psychological problem.

—*Robert Pasahow, PhD*

* * *

Many troubling disorders of the head and inner ear—such as dizziness, hearing loss and ringing in the ears—cause patients untold suffering, even though conventional medical doctors have ruled out any health problem. That's where TFT can help.

By rebalancing the body's energy pathways, TFT addresses the underlying cause of inner ear disturbances—which are many—to bring about relief.

 ## 50 Million People Hear Noise Inside Their Head

I noticed the ringing in my right ear at about the same time I became aware of a hearing loss in that ear. That was over six years ago. I had been using a telephone headset on my right ear for several years, and my first indication of a hearing problem was the need to increase the volume on the headset.

At first, the ringing noise was very annoying.

The ringing in my ear consists of constantly changing frequencies. I play a musical instrument and at first I spent a lot of time trying to match the pitch vocally. The sound level and pitch change from a variety causes. The more relaxed I am, for example, the lower the frequencies and overall volume of the ringing. Sometimes the noise is masked by other sound around me—such as, conversation, television or radio. Sometimes the noise is like the roar of traffic from the highway two miles away. At other times, the sound is screaming inside my head. I have always been thankful that the ringing is only in one ear.

Before treating tinnitus with TFT, we must recognize it as a symptom and be aware of the causes for it.

An estimated 50 million people in the USA suffer from tinnitus·. If that statistic holds true worldwide, then slightly over one billion people suffer from the disorder. Of these, 25% suffer tinnitus so severely that it affects their quality of life by constantly interfering with concentration, recreational activities, sleep and personal relationships. Sometimes, the inner noise is so bad that sufferers commit suicide.

∗ This data comes from the International Radiosurgery Support Association.

We can trace some causes of tinnitus to damage from excessive noise, acoustic neuromas, diabetes, common drugs like aspirin, some 200 prescription and nonprescription drugs which list tinnitus as a side effect, ear wax buildup, sinus infections, allergies, jaw misalignments, cardiovascular disease, underactive thyroid, head and neck trauma, surgical injury and Meniere's disease.

Many people with tinnitus also have hearing loss. Normal hearing may somewhat "mask" the sound of the tinnitus, as many people say their tinnitus is worse as their hearing loss increases. Indeed, even when the hearing nerve is severed resulting in total hearing loss, patients often still have tinnitus and may perceive it as having worsened.

Tinnitus is thought to be incurable, but drug therapies have been developed for it.

In my own case, my hearing loss and tinnitus were symptoms of an acoustic neuroma. It is thought that the tumor had been growing for about 10 years when the symptoms became noticeable. I had the tumor treated by Gamma Knife radiosurgery. This kind of tumor is never malignant and only becomes life-threatening when it puts pressure on the brain stem. But because the tumor exists within the bony structure of the head and the heat created by the radiation treatment causes swelling in the tumor that is slow to disburse, an MRI has difficulty determining the results of treatment, even after several years. When one of my semi-annual MRI's showed a slight increase in the size of the overall tumor, probably from swelling, my neurologist was talking about the need for additional Gamma Knife treatment.

That's when I contacted Dr. Callahan, based on the results he has had with TFT for tumors. Dr. Callahan treated me with great results for the tumor itself, the trauma associated with it, the fear associated with having to have the Gamma Knife treatment repeated, and so on. My last MRI showed for the first time no increase in the size of the tumor.

—Sharron Kanter

* * *

What's the ultimate cause of troubling disorders? For most non-genetic cases, it's usually an overload of toxins in our environment—both recognized and unrecognized. We call this overload the "barrel effect"—the body's ability to handle only a limited load of stressors. Once the barrel is full—whether from toxins, mold, environmental stress, job loss, relationship stress—our body's systems break down, eventually causing illness.

TFT, on the other hand, works with the body's own healing systems to alleviate the stress of these toxins. Unlike modern medical science or the newest drug being touted, TFT stimulates nature's healing system—our own body—to bring about relief.

One of our favorite stories is one that's very close to home—right down the street, in fact, at our veterinarian's office. In this case, continual tapping with TFT sequences and removal of toxins from the patient's environment alleviated a debilitating condition.

Let's take a look:

 ## Surgery Isn't the Only Solution

When one of our dogs fell ill, I called our veterinarian's office for an appointment. Unfortunately, our dog wasn't the only one sick that day. Our vet, too, was at home—sick with a unusual illness. When he returned my phone call to talk about our dog, I sympathetically asked him about his situation.

"I have Ménière's disease," he said—an inner-ear imbalance which is usually accompanied by extreme vertigo, nausea and progressive hearing loss, usually in one ear.

While he had been seen several times by doctors at a major university medical school, their only hope for him was to surgically severe his auditory nerve. While that would certainly eliminate the vertigo and nausea, it would also render him deaf in that ear. If he were to get Ménière's disease in the other ear, progressive hearing loss would eventually render him completely deaf. Not surprisingly, he hadn't yet made the decision to move forward with surgery to sever the nerve.

On the day I talked with him, the condition had gotten so bad, he had asked his internist to come over and give him injections of Compazine to reduce the nausea. But even then he wasn't able to go to work. He said his acupuncturist could relieve the symptoms for short time, but they always came right back.

This gave us a clue that perhaps something else was at work on his inner ear.

I told him that we had had great success with the symptoms of Ménière's, then asked if he would like Roger to treat it.

He was willing to try TFT, and Roger was able to quickly eliminate the symptoms within just a few minutes. Roger then started investigating what could be aggravating it.

As it turns out, the water pills his doctors had given him were toxic for him. The hypoallergenic pillow he had been sleeping on was another toxin. So we quickly used the 7-Second Toxin Treatment for the water pills, then asked him to change pillows, which at least enabled him to go to work the next day.

Over the next three months, his Ménière's symptoms would periodically return, leading Roger to treat him for several newly identified toxins. Each time, the symptoms quickly disappeared. And eventually, after three months, his Ménière's symptoms were gone. Interestingly, the autoclave solution his office used to sterilize the surgical equipment was a toxin for him, as was his laundry detergent.

When he went back to the university hearing clinic three months later, he learned that further hearing loss had also stopped. In other words, the progression of the disease had been halted.

TFT, working with nature's healing system, allowed his body to mend.

During his recovery period, he was very diligent about staying away from toxins, but his wife said later that, once his body was healed, he could again eat those things that had previously been toxic for him and even use some household chemicals which had previously been toxic. But as soon as his veterinary partner went on vacation and he had to work overtime, his body became overstressed and no longer had the ability to deal with those toxins.

Fifteen years later, this man is still our veterinarian. And he's still doing well.

What a wonderful option to have something natural and non-invasive to use in eliminating the symptoms of Ménière's disease, rather than severing the auditory nerve. Not only that, it's a great testimony to the lasting effects of TFT.

—*Joanne Callahan*

* * *

When we see troubling disorders that are simple—such as the recurring panic attacks described in our next case study—we usually know in advance that a toxin is at fault.

TFT can calm these attacks while we go to work with the patient to uncover the toxins present. Of course, as we'll find out, it's always better for the patient to discover on their own which are the culprits!

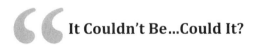

It Couldn't Be...Could It?

When a young professional man sought treatment for frequent panic attacks, I knew at once that a toxin was likely at work. The panic episodes awakened him at night, and were most prevalent in the early morning upon awakening. He also occasionally had them while driving to work.

Using the TFT sequence for panic, we rapidly brought down the panic symptoms from a "10" on the SUD scale to a "0."

Still, the actual source of the attacks remained a mystery. He recalled not actually experiencing them on a trip—which he attributed to being on vacation, relaxed and not having to go to work. He confessed a liking for his job and had not considered it too stressful until he tried to determine why he was having panic attacks. He was even beginning to suspect that maybe his wife was somehow making him anxious, though he reported a compatible and satisfying relationship. Still he couldn't make sense out of why he had the attacks at home, and most especially, in the bedroom.

Using Arthur Coca's pulse test—developed in 1994 and used by many TFT practitioners—our young man was able to test for various toxins at home as he encountered them. He found that in contrast to most people, his pulse rate was highest when he awakened, after which it would decline while he was at work, with occasional spikes of twenty or more points after lunch or coffee break. He discovered sensitivity to his occasional decaffeinated coffee and diet decaffeinated cola through his pulse variations, and went on a trial—taking those out of his diet for eight weeks which eliminated the occasional daytime spikes.

Then the actual cause of his panic attacks became clear.

After a significant reduction in his pulse from washing all his bedding, he realized that it could be his two cats—which he adored. In fact, they slept or scampered on his bed at night, and he always played with them before driving off to work.

He called me excitedly the morning after washing his bedding, vacuuming the room and drapes, and keeping his cats out of the bedroom for the night. He finally had a normal pulse and had experienced no panic episodes upon awakening. He later reported no panic attacks for a week, and then for a month—though they had previously been a daily occurrence. His panic episodes in the car also stopped after he started lint-brushing his clothes and washing his hands before leaving the house.

He told me it was a good thing he made the discovery about his cats through his own detective work. If I had suggested his beloved cats were contributing to his panic attacks and that he should keep them out of his bedroom as a test, he declared, he would have told me to go to Hell!

—Caroline E. Sakai, PhD

* * *

While so many troubling disorders can start to heal in just minutes with Thought Field Therapy, some people—because they don't know about TFT—exist for years without getting relief from conditions they have had since childhood.

In this inspiring story of one woman's journey, we see literally a lifetime of pain, discomfort, and botched medical procedures by well-meaning doctors as she searches for a cure.

 ## 24 Years of Searching for a Better Way to Breathe

To begin this story, I must go back to my youth in Montevideo, Uruguay when I was seven or eight years old. By then I was chronically allergic, with recurring asthmatic crises throughout a complicated childhood.

I never could breathe normally through my nose, and this reduced nasal breathing actually affected the development of the middle third portion of my face.

I had constant nasal obstructions and mucus. According to my doctors, the condition appeared to be a consequence of bronchial obstruction—particularly due to coughing and phlegm. They removed my tonsils, after which—when combined with an obstructed chest and nose—my breathing became forced and thoroughly uncomfortable.

Although the frequent asthmatic crises I had might seem serious, to me they were more "controllable" because they came and went, whereas the rhinitis· that my doctors eventually diagnosed was constant. They always considered rhinitis to be less important, but to me it wasn't, and I spent day and night searching for a way to breathe easily through my nose.

The cause of my rhinitis went through several diagnoses.

At first, doctors thought I has sinusitis and the treatment was vague and inefficient: medicines, drops, x-rays, exudates, various homeopathic doses, and self-vaccines recommended by

---

* Rhinitis is commonly known as a stuffy nose, but in its chronic state, patients suffer ongoing irritation and inflammation of the internal areas of the nose, excessive mucus, runny nose, nasal congestion and post-nasal drip. Recent studies say more than 50 million Americans suffer rhinitis. It also causes sleeping disorders, ear disorders, and even learning problems in children.

specialists. I had skin tests. I had to keep a record of my diet, then be punished with multiple visits to the doctor who imposed dietary restrictions in order to find the cause—but to no avail. The cure took too long, and eventually never arrived.

I lived through childhood, puberty, and youth, and my rhinitis was still there, always uncomfortable, but I didn't give up.

I consulted various ear-nose-and-throat specialists and allergists. I trusted them fully, and volunteered to undergo any necessary surgery. I still remember an infiltration treatment I once had, as traumatic as it was useless. I sat with my head against a wall, while the doctor unloaded various milliliters of corticoids through my nostrils with a syringe which actually broke inside my nose. This indescribably awful—and useless—experience resulted in a later intranasal cauterization which, again, yielded no positive results.

Believe me, I tried everything, and yet I still did not give up.

I could have easily stopped my attempts and simply gotten used to breathing through my mouth, as so many others have had to do. But I always felt the need to find relief.

The only thing that brought me some relief—though artificial and temporary—were common nasal drops. Everybody I know told me to stop using them, but no one offered a better solution. I spent what felt like ages unable to go through the day (or night) without using the drops to avoid anxiety. I found ways to have a dropper with me at all times: in my purse, in my underclothes, during class, at a dance, at the beach and on my night table. Imagine the countless embarrassing situations I faced when the effect of the drops wore off and I spoke again in a nasal drawl. Even worse, whenever I had to use the drops in public, I then had to listen to everybody's advice, although nobody offered solutions or even understanding.

Some years ago, willing as usual to try anything to free myself from this suffering, I followed a rumor and went to a place where they sold some clandestine healing powder. I was forbidden to have Cola drinks during the treatment, and was even warned that it could also lead to an increase in appetite and weight gain. Though I was already overweight, I gave it a try and for a time, it worked. A year later, however, my symptoms returned and I returned to the pseudo-clinic, where they strengthened the dose. The result was a gain of 5 kg in one week, so I abandoned the treatment once and for all.

Eventually, I met Isabel Aguilar, who has not only helped me through a number of hardships in my life, she has also helped me achieve many goals in the years since I first met her.

At 31 years old, living alone and finally having time to work on myself, I decided to go beyond everything I had attempted before and finally find a cure for my illness.

Little did I know that with Isabel and Thought Field Therapy, in just a few minutes and then with some practice on my part, I could become a liberated woman again.

I am truly grateful.

—as told to María Isabel Aguilar

* * *

Of course, not everyone suffers decades of pain and discomfort as this young woman did, but unfortunately *many do.* That's why it has become our mission to bring the healing capabilities of TFT to people around the world. In this work, we meet countless patients who get relief—not only for the troubling disorder they've decided to "work on," but with other conditions that are secondary to their main illness.

For instance, we're reminded of the story of one woman who attended a practitioners training only to see her own fibromyalgia and back pain improve as a side benefit to learning the tapping sequences and studying them for her work.

"My massage therapist was amazed at the difference in the quality of my muscles," Katharyn Meyers said. "They didn't have the knotty quality of a fibromyalgia patient, and for the first time in two years, she was able to give me a real massage working on deeper layers of tissue without the horrible pain I'd experienced previously."

This was especially remarkable to Katharyn because, as she said, "I never did work specifically on fibromyalgia. The relief from FM was a side benefit!" It was the first time in over 20 years she had gotten relief from the awful pain associated with fibromyalgia.

Tapping Away the Stress That
Causes Troubling Disorders

You'll find videos that step you through the complete tapping sequences for eliminating troubling disorders at our website:

www.rogercallahan.com/pathways

Chapter Eight:
TFT for Serious and
Life-Threatening Illnesses

Life-threatening illnesses such as cancer, arteriosclerosis and heart disease are often the result of a lifetime of poor nutrition, lack of exercise, environmental factors and other stressors that impact the body's immune system. Like the "barrel effect" we talked about in the last chapter, the body gets so full of toxins that it can no longer fend off serious illness. Our bodies become a breeding ground for life-threatening conditions.

Staying healthy means you must take charge of your own habits and lifestyle decisions.

But, as we'll see in this chapter, it's not always possible to give up smoking, lose weight, and make good choices on your own. That's where TFT can help.

Not only that, but when illness does strike, TFT can help speed recovery from life-threatening illness or conditions—by calming the stress and anxiety, clearing the body's natural healing pathways, and minimizing the toxic affects of the medications a patient must take to get better.

In our first story, a woman survives a harrowing brush with cancer—after doctors give her just a 6% chance to live. As her life force ebbs, Thought Field Therapy, surrogate tapping· and a last-minute intervention by telephone with Roger brings her back to health and a vibrant new outlook on life.

 Letting the Immune System Do Its Job

I remember the day Joyce was diagnosed with cancer. The doctors called it Chronic Myeloid Leukemia, an interchange of

---

* Surrogate tapping is the TFT technique of touching the patient—or holding them, as in the case of a small child—while tapping out the sequence on your own body. Or, a practitioner might tap out a sequence on you as you touch or hold someone who is ill and could benefit from TFT.

the tails of the 9 and 22 chromosomes that produces leukemic cells in the blood and enormous numbers of white blood cells.

Possible life expectancy? Five to eight years.

Due to the requirements of the Health Act of Australia, the only course of action was to keep the cancer under control with the drug Hydroxyurea taken orally. This became quite a balancing act in adjusting the dosage between daily, then weekly, blood tests until the white cell counts came close to normal.

As we sought all kinds of alternate therapies, the required tests became less and less frequent. As for conventional therapies, there were none. A T-cell transplant was the only other option if a perfect match was to be found—and that "if" was too big to rely on.

We threw ourselves into macrobiotic cooking classes, acupuncture and herbal remedies. Popping pills, drinking juice, being pricked with acupuncture needles, as well as other needles sucking the lifeblood out of her—not to mention drilling holes in her hip and sternum for blood marrow tests year after year. All of it was beginning to reduce Joyce's morale especially when one blood test revealed a virus in the blood carried by mosquitoes called Ross River Fever.

At the time, I was suffering from Chronic Fatigue Syndrome, Irritable Bowel Syndrome and Ross River Fever while still operating our three florist shops. We also cared for my 84-year-old mother who had been sent home from the hospital with a Golden Staph Infection following a broken hip operation. The dressing had to be changed up to three times a day.

It was almost more than a family could handle.

But we were determined to beat our problems. One evening in front of the television for a brief respite, we saw what we thought must be a miracle on a news program. A young lady with a fear of snakes was—within minutes of this fellow curing her of her phobia—handling the snake in her hands and around her neck. *It must be a set-up,* we thought.

Still, with skepticism on our minds but desperate for a cure, we sought out this fellow who introduced us to a miraculous modality called Thought Field Therapy. I immediately signed up for the upcoming seminar.

After being told by the medical profession for more than 10 years that there was no cure for leukemia, it was difficult for us to understand how a few 'taps' here and there could possibly make a difference. But I attended alone and by late on the second day, I began to notice being more relaxed and able to think more clearly.

Meanwhile, my wife was incorporating more and more alternative therapies into her regimen which helped to control her white blood cell count. To her, tapping seemed a waste of time, but suddenly her cancer turned acute and moved into the Blast-Crisis stage. Having been given just five days to live, Joyce was admitted to an eight-month hospital stay for eight rounds of chemotherapy, along with treatment with the drug Gleevec.

Every listed side effect of the drug, she experienced. Still others have surfaced since. They performed all the usual tests on her—ECG, x-rays, blood tests, lumbar puncture and bone marrow test. After 11 preliminary days in the hospital, she received her first round of chemotherapy.

The sheer volume of drugs they gave her was immense. On top of blood and platelet transfusions were injections into the stomach of Neutrophil (a type of white blood cell), 24-hour antibiotic drip, plus six other tablets twice a day for nausea, heart, and throat problems (caused by the Gleevec).

I quickly contacted Dr. Roger Callahan and together with my limited knowledge of the TFT sequences and the 7-Second Toxin Treatment, Roger and I were able to put a program together. Alas, Joyce was too weak and ill to even bother. Three days after her first round of chemotherapy, she was admitted to Intensive Care with a pulse rate of 200 and a temperature of 104°.

Five injections of adrenaline within six hours calmed her pulse, and soon she was back in the Oncology Ward with an injection of morphine for pains in her legs. She began to explain to the family members present how beautiful the white light was shining through the angels wings flying through the ICU ward.

She's near death, I thought, as my blood pressure soared. Tapping the TFT sequence for Extended Trauma was the only thing that kept me from being admitted as a patient right along with her.

That night, two hours of surrogate tapping· resulted in a turnaround in Joyce's condition until she was able to do some of the tapping herself. Embarrassed but motivated, we decided tap and do the 7-Second Toxin Treatment for all medications injected into Joyce's body.

My wife refused all chemotherapy treatments after that first round. At the end of six weeks, she was allowed to go home but because her blood counts were so low as a result of taking Gleevec, an infection set in which put her back in the hospital again.

After just eight weeks total in the hospital—and one round of chemotherapy—Joyce left the hospital and has never been an in-patient for cancer again.

With tapping and affirmations, the 7-Second Toxin Treatment, and alkaline foods and beverages, Joyce and I don't just believe in a cure for cancer, we know there is a cure for all disease by letting the immune system do its job.

Fifteen years and 10 bone marrow tests later, Joyce has a full set of perfect female chromosomes again.

Statistics show she is one of just 6% to survive Chronic Myeloid Leukemia in the Blast-Crisis stage. We celebrated 49 years of marriage last month and now convey our gratitude to Eugene Piccinotti and his wife Karen who first introduced us to TFT.

Thank you, Roger Callahan, for your help at our crisis point. We are healthy here 'Down Under.'

—Ron and Joyce Tate

* * *

Cancer is a traumatic and frightening diagnosis for most people. But just as we've seen in Joyce's story, TFT can help the body's own immune system do its job, ridding the body of the cancerous cells and returning it to a healthy state.

· Surrogate tapping is the TFT technique of touching the patient—or holding them, as in the case of a small child—while tapping out the sequence on your own body. Or, a practitioner might tap out a sequence on you as you touch or hold someone who is ill and could benefit from TFT.

But what about the other reality of cancer—the toxic and necessary medications that cause nausea, hair loss and other side effects? TFT can stimulate the body's natural healing ability to ward off the worst effects of these drugs—keeping the patient stronger, less stressed, less depressed and with a healthier appetite.

We know first-hand the horrible side effects of necessary medications—especially chemotherapy drugs—because Joanne is a Stage IV cancer survivor, now cancer-free for more than nine years. Her story will give you insight into how TFT works to aid cancer patients.

 ## The Road Less Traveled

Most of us wonder as we see pharmaceutical ads on television, "Why would anyone want to take that medication if you get all those side-effects from it?"

Yet there are some instances when a necessary medication must be taken to improve one's health. Using TFT to eliminate the side-effects of those medications not only greatly improves the quality of life of the patient, it also improves compliance with doctor's orders. We've found that TFT can successfully eliminate the negative side-effects of necessary medications without interfering with their effectiveness. In fact, we learned and fine-tuned this TFT protocol when I had Stage IV Non-Hodgkins Lymphoma and was required to take Interferon.

At the same time, one of our training participants was taking a very strong combination of medications for AIDS. We were able to eliminate his side-effects, as well. He is the only patient alive (after 8½ years) out of his test group of 34 patients—and I have been cancer-free for nearly 9 years.

We have since eliminated the side effects of many other necessary medications including chemotherapy and steroidal injections.

Our first case—in which we really fine tuned the protocol— was with my own prescription for Interferon, an injectible immune-stimulating drug for cancer and Hepatitis C patients. If you're not familiar with that medication, it produces severe flu-like symptoms. It makes one ache to the very core of their being. In fact, the medication's side-effects are so notorious, when they prescribed it for me they also handed me a prescription for Prozac and said, "You will probably need this." Not knowing anything about Interferon, but knowing I could use TFT, I said "No, thank you," to the Prozac.

About six hours after my first injection, I felt like I had been run over by a monster truck. In addition, I had severe nausea and the chills. We immediately tried to treat the symptoms and were able to reduce it somewhat. I felt pretty miserable, but just about the time the side-effects wore off, it was time for the next injection. This next time, we used TFT to "detox" me from the shot immediately after I injected it—going through the entire toxin treatment procedures.

I had no side-effects whatsoever after that second injection.

What we discovered is that, if we treated the toxicity of the Interferon at the time the injection was administered, I would have no side-effects. But if we forgot—because the phone rang or some other distraction came up, for example—the more time that lapsed between the injection and doing the TFT detox sequence, the more side-effects I suffered. I took Interferon injections for nearly two years, without the negative side-effects so commonly reported. And it did the job it was prescribed for, stimulating my immune system.

About the same time, in fact right after my cancer diagnosis, a young man attended our Diagnostic Level training in California. During our routine demonstrations of TFT diagnosis, we saw he had an unusually low HRV reading and we mentioned that to him. He then revealed he was taking nitro-glycerin for heart problems, along with medication for AIDS. He was on a particularly strong AIDS cocktail and each time he took it, he suffered from nausea, convulsions and severe diarrhea. But his doctor had ordered it for him and about 34 other individuals who were taking this particular form of the medication.

We offered to do a demonstration on the TFT toxin treatment with his medications since I was having excellent results with it for Interferon. He agreed and the next morning came to class with his pills in hand. We demonstrated the toxin treatment on him at the time he took his pills. He suffered no reaction from them that day—and did not have another reaction from that medication for nearly a year, at which time he repeated the treatment.·

While the frequency with which he and I needed to use the TFT toxin treatment varied considerably, the result was we both had a drastically improved quality of life. I have had no recurrence of my cancer, and he is the only patient still alive of the 34 in his medication group. It appears that TFT did not interfere with the efficacy of these medications.

—*Joanne Callahan*

* * *

Another side effect associated with the cancer itself is pain. Unending, intractable pain. But while medications—even morphine—sometimes fail to alleviate the agony, we have had great success in providing relief using Thought Field Therapy.

Relieving the Suffering of Cancer Patients

I have worked with a number of cancer patients over the years with intractable pain. In the cases referred to me, the various drugs and medications were giving little or no help. The first few times I treated severe pain, many years ago, I was quite surprised to find that I could reduce, or even completely eliminate pain in some advanced cases of cancer when some very strong drugs and meds did not give relief.

I recall a cancer patient who was working with a TFT trainee to relieve the pain of metastasized kidney cancer. Medication gave no relief in this case. And while the TFT therapist was able to reduce the chronic severe pain from a "10" to a "7"—for which the patient was thrilled—it would not go any lower. The

---

* You can read his entire story, in his own words, at www.rogercallahan.com/pathways.

therapist called me for Voice Technology (VT) support (as a good many of our diagnostic level trainees do when working with difficult clients). Within minutes, I was able to completely eliminate every trace of pain with the more refined VT. All three of us were quite pleased with this outcome.

Recently, I treated another very severe case of chronic cancer pain. The physicians on the case were using morphine and though it often gives profound relief, in this case it did not do much at all. Unlike most cases I treat, where total relief is almost instantaneous, it took a day and a half to realize a slight reduction of pain in this instance—due to what I call inertial delay. The pain continued to progressively reduce, without further treatment, until it was totally gone over the next few days.

When I first discovered my pain treatment about 17 years ago, I assumed that I was somehow simply blocking the awareness of the pain. Today, due to experience over the years, I believe that we are doing something fundamentally corrective and actually eliminating the cause of the pain at its deepest source.

Discovering that one has cancer is a very frightening experience. I recommend that cancer patients tap out the TFT sequence for the trauma of having cancer, along with any other psychological sources of stress.

While I am discussing cancer patients, I should mention the common symptom of anorexia that often accompanies radiation or chemotherapy. The inability to eat can greatly weaken an already weak cancer patient. Just as when we treat *anorexia nervosa* patients (typically young women who are literally starving themselves to death), we are able to treat cancer patients to eliminate all traces of the averse reaction to food. Typically, such a patient will express hunger and begin eating immediately after the treatment; this is very helpful for building up the general strength of the patient.

I often treat patients when they are going for frightening diagnostic tests that will determine whether or not they have cancer, and I typically will get them feeling very strong and unafraid of the test, as well as unafraid of the possible outcome. It's surprising that TFT treatments can do this since objectively, the tests and their implications, are understandably scary. This result shows that our treatments can make ordinary people unusually strong when facing possible disasters. After successful treatment, patients report that they hope for the best, but the worst news will not throw them!

Many people have a number of fears centering on necessary surgery. This is understandable.

I will never forget years ago, when a friend of mine, without advance notice, was rushed into cancer surgery and was understandably quite tense about it. His wife accompanied him to the hospital and phoned me from there. She asked me to give him a quick treatment over the phone. He was very relaxed after the TFT treatment and actually slept in the pre-surgery room. When the nurse came in to give him tranquilizers, he did not need them.

The surgery was very successful.

I had another client who was an anesthesiologist. He told me that the greatest danger during surgery was fear. Mind you, he was not referring to phobic or inappropriate fear, but rather the quite appropriate and intense fear that accompanies any major surgery.

—Roger J. Callahan, PhD

*   *   *

With trained TFT therapists working around the globe, Thought Field Therapy meets its share of cancer patients. But no story better illustrates the ability of TFT to rebalance the body's natural healing systems and remove fear in cancer patients than this one from a practitioner in the United Kingdom.

"Whatever You're Doing, Keep Doing It!"

After three sessions of chemotherapy, my client was deemed too weak to continue. She had been diagnosed with a particularly virulent and invasive case of sarcoma—cancer of the lungs. Over the previous nine months, she'd been on 15 different medications until finally, she developed Tachycardia, an abnormally rapid heartbeat.

Clearly her body had had enough.

As an ex-psychiatric nurse accustomed to practicing hypnotherapy, neuro-linguistic programming, counseling and Reiki healing techniques, "Candace" was in tune with her own body and could easily notice subtle changes in her energy states. Not only could she give me good feedback during our TFT sessions, but she was exemplary with following through at home.

In short, she was the ideal TFT client.

During our first session, she expressed feelings of low self-esteem and sadness about the cancer. Then, a distant memory surfaced. It was quite obvious to both of us she had a lot of trauma to clear—which I did using the appropriate tapping sequences.

During our next session, I tested her current medications for toxicity and found that all of them indeed showed as toxic for her. I applied the 7-Second Toxin Treatment· for each and asked her to tap out the treatment every time she took a tablet.

Further diagnostic told me that she felt undeserving about recovering from cancer—in fact, she neither felt safe to be over it nor that it was time to be over it.

Her homework was to tap for cancer every couple of hours and do a further TFT sequence 3 times a day.

By the next session, a quick diagnostic test with a voltmeter† showed that her right lung was showing neutral, and her left lung was giving a positive reading. She told me that she had been tapping every few hours. Since she had stopped chemotherapy treatments, TFT and her own knowledge of relaxation techniques and herbal formulations were the only treatment she was receiving.

Progress was slow, but steady.

As a client, I have to say that Candace was one of my more unusual ones. She was still suffering from numerous traumas in

---

* You can find details about the 7-Second Toxin Treatment at www.rogercallahan.com/pathways.
† A voltmeter is a common device that measures positive or negative polarity—in this case, within the body's tissues. Harrold Saxton Burr pioneered the use of the voltmeter as a tool to measure for negative polarity which correlated with malignancy in gynaecological tumors.

her past—and even felt that she had carried hurts from a past life into this current one. As a practitioner, I did not judge the validity or probability of this—but rather, dealt with these revelations as part of the "reality" she was living and suffering under at that time.

She had not received kindness from her parents, and instead was made to feel guilty and inadequate. Although she excelled at school, she was kept back a year in order for others in her class to catch up, which she resented. Not only did she feel sadness over this, but she believed that it had caused her problems later in life. I used TFT to clear these traumas.

She also believed that, at some point in a past life, she had been crushed to death and was therefore experiencing feelings of loneliness, abandonment, betrayal, loss, bereavement and sadness in this one. These feelings, she said, were tied up with the nausea she was experiencing—as every time she thought about the nausea, she felt these emotional hurts, too. I used TFT to clear these emotions as I would with any others—regardless of their origin. When I re-tested her with TFT diagnostic procedures, she was strong.

During the next session, my diagnostics still showed a negative reading on both sides of her lung—the site of the cancer. When I asked her what had occurred over the last few days, she described additional unresolved traumas that I had not treated her for previously.

Not surprisingly, she had several layers of trauma associated with the cancer, so I used advanced TFT sequences to clear them. Candace also told me a memory had surfaced that she believed was making her nausea more severe: As a child she had been spanked in the bathroom after she had been sick. As we cleared her feelings of sadness, three other incidents presented themselves in her mind. We worked steadily until she could no longer feel any distress associated with these past incidents.

Candace had not been out of the house due to her illness—except for doctors appointments and tests—and she had started to experience some agoraphobia*. When she thought about going out, she felt panic. We quickly tapped out the TFT sequences for phobia and trauma until the feelings cleared.

I took a voltmeter reading at the end of the session and found that both sides of her lungs were registering as positive.

At this point, I began to be cautiously excited.

The next day, Candace received the results of a scan and it showed that the lung cancer was receding. Her surgeon commented, "I don't know what you're doing, but keep doing it!"

We continued to work on clearing past hurts and supporting her body's natural healing capabilities by removing and neutralizing as many toxins as possible.

Chocolate was a toxin we immediately identified that she had been eating to keep her weight up. And now, since her last treatment session, she had developed a bad taste in her mouth that seemed to occur every day. She had been eating other sweets which all tested as toxic, and she agreed to stop eating them. She and her husband were also having a lot of work done to the house—which added toxins to her home environment. Formaldehyde was one culprit, as were petrochemicals and pesticides. She had also recently had a flu vaccine, and was put onto a new tablet for her nausea. I also found that malt bread, eggs, milk and sugar were toxins. I used the 7-Second Toxin Treatment for them all.

Two weeks later, I received a phone call from Candace who told me that the results of her latest scan had come back.

No active cancer could be found!

Her specialist was baffled by the result and could not explain how she could show such a result without chemotherapy.

—*Ildiko Scurr*

* * *

---

* Agoraphobia is an abnormal fear of open or public places, such that sufferers rarely leave their home or even their bedroom.

Cancer isn't the only life-threatening illness that Thought Field Therapy can help. By working with the body's own energy pathways and natural healing systems, TFT quickly brings the body into balance so that it is stronger and more able to ward off serious illness. Under these less stressed conditions, the body's own immune system, lymph system and other systems finally have the energy and resources to eliminate disease.

But what about when the body experiences a "mechanical breakdown" such as a blocked artery or dysfunctional heart valve? TFT can help there, too, by minimizing the stress of an attack or the stress of recovery when doctors must surgically correct the defect.

Even in critical situations, as the next story will show, TFT calms the stress associated with a life-threatening attack giving the patient time to connect with emergency medical personnel.

 ## "Is There a Doctor On Board?"

I was flying home to Los Angeles from a trip to India when, about three hours west of the airport over the Pacific Ocean, the captain announced there was a medical emergency on the plane and requested that any nurse or doctor on board report to the nearest crew member.

Although I am a registered nurse, I didn't pay much attention since this was a full flight on a jumbo jetliner and I presumed there would be a number of doctors on the plane. After a short while, however, I realized that the medical emergency was just across the aisle from where I was sitting and there didn't seem to be anyone besides the crew assisting the individual. I walked over and was told that no doctor had come forward.

The 90-year-old Indian woman was in considerable distress.

She was pale and gasping for breath and her skin was cold and clammy. The crew had brought out a tank of oxygen and we placed an oxygen mask on her immediately. Her pulse was over 130 and her blood pressure was 90/50 which I initially interpreted as a good sign, until her daughter told me that her normal blood pressure was 200/120. Her pulse seemed regular, however, and I could not detect any ectopic beats or arrhythmia, which was reassuring, since there was no cardiac monitor on board to show us what her heart was doing.

The airplane medical kit provided by the crew contained a stethoscope, however, and when I listened to her lungs I realized she was in the midst of congestive heart failure as her lungs were full of fluid.

Her daughter told me that she had previously had cardiac bypass surgery and normally took large doses of various medications, but that she had gone off her schedule due to the time changes, and most of her medications were in her suitcases which she had checked through to Los Angeles.

I learned from the crew that there was no defibrillator or oxygen bag on board which would be needed if she went into cardiac arrest before we landed. However, we did have enough oxygen to make it three hours to Los Angeles.

About that time, an Australian physician appeared. He asked me what kind of nurse I was, and I told him I was a neonatal nurse. I asked him what kind of doctor he was, and he said he was a pediatrician.

"Great," we said in unison as we looked at each other.

We began going through the airplane's medical bag and found a vial of Lasix—a diuretic. Finding a vein in her arm, we gave her an intravenous dose of the Lasix to help take the fluid off her lungs. We then asked the captain to call ahead and arrange to have an ambulance waiting for the plane at LAX.

Given the limited medical resources on the airplane, there was nothing further we could do except hope that she didn't go into cardiac arrest before we landed.

Then I remembered Thought Field Therapy which I had learned from TFT trainer Mary Cowley and from reading Dr. Callahan's book.

Since there was nothing else to be done, I started tapping out the TFT sequences. The woman looked at me as if I were crazy, but she was still gasping for air and dripping with perspiration— really in far too much distress to pay much attention to what I was doing. I tapped out the sequences for about 30 minutes until I noticed that her skin had changed from cold and clammy to warm and dry—and her respirations had slowed and become relatively easy. I then re-checked her pulse, which had dropped to 90, and her blood pressure, which had gone up to 160/90 (apparently more in her normal range). While I had performed the TFT sequences, she had also gradually relaxed from a state of extreme distress to a state of relative comfort.

Her daughter, who was translating from Hindi to English, confirmed that she was feeling much better.

I checked on her every half hour or so until we landed, and she remained comfortable for the rest of the flight. I cannot say how this incident would have turned out had I not performed the TFT treatment, but I was very pleased to see how quickly her condition turned around following the treatment. The physician and I had initially felt it was very likely that, given her age, medical history and clinical presentation, she would go into cardiac arrest before we reached LAX.

At the end of the flight, the airlines presented me with a beautiful silk scarf to thank me for my assistance.

—Kristina Hancock

* * *

One of the most common "mechanical" breakdowns in the human body is stroke—a blockage in one of the arteries leading to the brain that robs the brain of critical oxygen. Brain swelling occurs, tissue is usually lost, and important functions such as speech, motor skills, muscle reactions, even memory can be severely impaired. Paralysis often occurs.

Not only is stroke the leading cause of adult disability in the United States and Europe, it is the #2 cause of death in the world.

Most people never recover their former lives.

But in this next story of a woman whose stroke impairment is among the worst we have seen in our professional careers, a TFT practitioner puts her on the road to recovering her speaking ability and using her arms again—20 years after her stroke!

The Road to Recovering a Happy Life

Upon hearing the news of her mother's sudden death, "Bridget" suffered a stroke. That was 20 years ago, and for the next two decades, she could neither move her arms nor speak or form words. Primitive grunts were the only sound she made, and a Lightwriter text-to-speech device was her only method of communication.

When I saw her she was still very upset about her mother and sobbed every time we spoke about her. She had arthritis in her knees which were painful and swollen. She had high blood pressure. Her medication was Dipyridamole (an anticoagulant), bendrofluozide (a diuretic), aspirin, Atonavastin for cholesterol control, and Diclofenac for arthritis.

She was frustrated and angry because of her condition.

She broke down in emotion, as she typed the words that told me of her mother's death. Her SUD was at a "10"—the highest level, even after 20 years. She could not stop thinking about her mother's death. It replayed like a video in her head day and night. She hardly ever smiled and didn't go out of the house very much.

She had to leave her husband and seven children in London to go into sheltered accommodation. Not surprisingly, she found tremendous guilt in this.

Tapping on her myself (as she could not use both her arms), I first treated Bridget for her mother's sudden death. She wept at first as she thought about it, but after the second tapping sequence, she declared, "It's going."

Her face began to light up and she smiled for the first time in ages. After the last tapping sequence, she started to laugh.

I next treated her for the shock of waking up in the hospital—not being able to speak—and for having left her husband and children behind. She was amazed at the difference in so short a treatment session. Later that week, Bridget's friend called to say she had never seen anything like it and that Bridget had spoken the word, "Mamma" when talking about her mother. She had never done that before, and it had been 20 years since the stroke!

When I visited Bridget for a follow up appointment, she had begun painting pictures on canvas using an artist's brush in her left hand! She was going out on her own and could be seen motoring around town on her mobility scooter—smiling and singing to herself.

Since TFT treatment, Bridget has a new, active, happy life. She goes shopping to town without any anxiety, and goes on holiday and on bus tours. She attended a local painting class. Everyone comments on how different she is. She even wants to go to New York! Not bad for someone who did not want to leave the house two weeks prior TFT.

She insists that I see her on a regular basis, as she has gained so much from the TFT treatments. Another breakthrough was that she could suddenly say her daughter's name. 'Janine'— which isn't easy for someone who lost their speech through stroke and has not spoken in 20 years!

—*Terry Perry*

Tapping for Serious, Life-Threatening Illnesses

You'll find videos at our website that step you through the complete tapping sequences for minimizing the negative side effects of medication, reducing the stress of treatment and eliminating the stress of individual energy toxins on the body. Visit:

www.rogercallahan.com/pathways

Chapter Nine:
Relieving Physical Pain

Millions of people suffer from physical pain every hour of every day. And whether it's back pain, joint pain, headaches, bursitis, old sports or military injuries, sinus pain or any other type, this ongoing physical pain robs them of a normal life, and worse, robs them of their spirit and sometimes even their will to live.

Unfortunately, many pain patients turn to painkilling drugs or experimental surgeries, usually emerging no better than they were before.

As an alternative to these demoralizing (and risky) options, TFT has proven extraordinarily effective at stopping physical pain in its tracks. Most importantly, TFT does no harm.

Even pain that results from injuries suffered years ago can be treated with Thought Field Therapy. And in the next several pages, you'll read, too, about pain which has no medical cause, but instead is caused by unresolved emotions and feelings trapped with the body's energy pathways. Let's take a look.

Time Is a Non-Existent Luxury

In primary-care medical practices, providing a patient with an hour of psychotherapy or other therapies that help with pain relief is a nonexistent luxury. Fifteen minutes or less with a patient is more often the norm.

Even "power therapies" such as EMDR· and hypnotherapy require more time to employ during a treatment session. When both time and office space are limited—as in a busy medical office—Thought Field Therapy becomes especially attractive given the few minutes it requires for treatment and the rapid effectiveness it shows in bringing about results.

---

* EMDR is Eye Movement Desensitization and Reprocessing—a form of psychotherapy that was developed to resolve symptoms of post-traumatic stress by re-processing distressing memories.

Working as I do in a busy primary-care practice with pain patients, I have found TFT to be readily adaptable to the time and space limitations of this setting. Here, the clinician must work quickly or not at all. I have found that TFT can be integrated with other treatments to create a powerful treatment package—as the following case will show.

"Ms. A" was a 29 year-old mother of two who had sustained neck and back injuries in a motor vehicle accident. She had been treated with physical therapy for six weeks since her accident, but neither her physical therapist nor her physician could get her to comply with a more active physical-therapy program. Their intentions were to gradually introduce a gentle exercise routine, massage therapy and gentle manipulations to improve movement and posture. Her physical therapist speculated that she might have suffered some psychological trauma in the past given her hypersensitivity to being touched and her marked stiffness and muscle-guarding behaviors. Her pain was clearly disproportionate to our diagnosis and she was relying heavily on "pain-killers."

My initial diagnosis further revealed impairment due to what she said was severe pain throughout her neck, shoulders, and upper, middle and lower back. She was stiff, too, since she usually avoided all movement out of fear of becoming re-injured.

The pain was only tolerable, she said, if she avoided moving.

At its worst, she rated her pain a "10" on a scale of 0 to 10. Additionally, she started feeling numbness and "pins and needles" in her arms and legs. Moreover, she commented that, "I'm feeling old" and "I can't do anything anymore" and even "I feel like I'm going to die."

When we began our TFT session, I asked her to observe the nature and quality of her pain sensations, then describe them to me. I asked her to focus on the point of greatest intensity of pain. Then I asked her to notice what was going on emotionally as she concentrated on the pain.

Once she was focused, I showed her each step in the TFT sequence for pain—then had her tap out each step on herself. She first tapped her left collarbone point about 30 times and reported that the pain diminished to about 6.5. Tapping the gamut spot on the back of her left hand brought the pain down to 5.5. When I asked her to tap again after repeating the phrase, "I deeply accept myself, even though I still have some pain left"— she was able to bring the pain down to 4.

So far, so good.

Unfortunately, at this point she disputed that the treatment would work long-term, saying, "I can get some relief now if I stay still, but I won't be able to stay like this when I start to move again."

I asked her how strongly she believed this—and how much it bothered her. She responded that it was very upsetting—at least an "8" on the SUD scale of 0 to 10 *(subjective units of distress).*

Asking her to think about the pain of movement, I quickly tapped out the TFT sequence for phobia which brought her SUD down to 1.5. Focusing next on the road accident itself, I used the TFT sequences for trauma and anger. Then I had her visualize moving around her house while taking care of her two year-old or doing light housework (which was when she reported having the most pain).

We went through the tapping sequences for pain, phobias, trauma and rage. Lastly, we went back to her current pain and tapped again, bringing it down to a "2."

When her physical therapist reported over the next few weeks that she was attending physical therapy more regularly and was starting range-of motion exercises, he asked me, "What did you do with her?"

"TFT," I answered, "TFT."

—Bruce N. Eimer, PhD
ABPP, Clinical Psychologist

* * *

Even pain that results from injuries suffered years ago can be treated with Thought Field Therapy. And while most of us have never played college sports—with all its repetitive injuries—our pain can sometimes persist just as intensely. In this next story about a college football player, just three sessions of TFT relieves the pain and improves range of motion.

Life After College

One of my clients is an ex-college football player who suffered severe neck pain with limited mobility in rotating his head to the left or right. This was all due to the great amounts of tackling and blocking during his many years of competitive football.

I used the standard TFT sequence for physical pain after testing him for *psychological reversal.* After just three treatment procedures, his neck pain was completely gone. Not only that, but he also had complete mobility in rotating his head.

I was astonished by these results.

I have monitored his neck condition over the last two months, and so far he has enjoyed the benefits of TFT to the fullest. I have not had to repeat the algorithms for this condition since the initial treatment.

—*Shad Meshad, MSW*
LCSW, CTS

* * *

Regardless of the type of original injury—and even regardless of the severity of the resulting pain—Thought Field Therapy can provide relief.

In this next story, a Catholic priest from Uganda reports on the effectiveness of TFT with victims in that war-torn region. After suffering physical abuse, surviving attacks by rebels, witnessing the deaths of fellow seminary students, and suffering the effects of indigenous diseases, the Ugandan priests, sisters and parishioners use TFT to rapidly reduce pain and the aftereffects of trauma.

A Letter From Uganda

There have been so many healings in Uganda by the TFT volunteer relief team. Almost everyone attending the initial training for religious staff got healed solely during the demonstrations of the TFT sequences. Many people with pain got healed—and they testified so, both the Christians, sisters and priests. One priest got healed of shoulder pain and another one of leg pain.

Those priests and sisters who had been traumatized by war rebels from 1996 to 2001—and more especially by the seminary attack in 1997 when 20 seminarians were abducted and 14 of them killed—were healed of trauma during the training.

Some parishioners were healed through surrogate treatment, such as one woman who was healed of pain at a long distance when someone else was being tapped. Many of those who had been trained as practitioners reported many healings for the people they treated—with joint pains and other pain. I saw with my own eyes a man get healed of serious malaria symptoms in Kilembe hospital. I was used as surrogate and the man—who could not stand or walk with strength—began doing everything by himself very strongly.

I thank you so much for sending us the TFT trainers. In Uganda, TFT has been successful for around 98% of victims. Better yet, for all trauma cases, TFT treatment was 100% successful for those healed during the trainings. I have also become fully trained in TFT after the refresher courses in Uganda—and am able to help many people become healed as a result.

I am really very happy, the people are happy and the bishop is very happy. He attended the training himself and healed one of his priests of trauma—reducing the SUD from 10 to 0.

It has been so wonderful to see so many immediate healings in a very short time. We are very grateful for your kindness and support—and for sending us a very good team. They did a very good job, were very committed and responsible, and knew what they were doing. They were even able to come down to the level of our local people in their training approach. I know TFT will flourish in Uganda.

—*Father Peter Mubunga Basaliza*

---

* Surrogate treatment or surrogate tapping refers to the TFT technique of touching the patient—or holding them, as in the case of a small child—while tapping out the sequence on your own body. Or, a practitioner might tap out a sequence on you as you touch or hold someone who is ill and could benefit from TFT.

* * *

Of course, most practitioners know that the trauma of a accident, injury or incident often causes *somatoform pain*—pain that isn't caused by tissue damage, inflammation or any other medical condition, but rather by the traumatic emotions that remain following the trauma.

In this next story, one patient *begins* suffering severe arthritic pain *over a year after* her physical injuries are healed. Interestingly, her naturopathic physician—who had succeeded in treating severe arthritic pain with a unique protocol he had developed—marvels at the speed with which TFT not only relieves arthritic pain, but also relieves the associated trauma, which he had not been able to do.

Relieving the Trauma That Causes Delayed Pain

In my experience, the onset of arthritis symptoms can usually be traced back to a traumatic life event that occurred in the past. An individual's arthritis may begin anywhere from 1½ to 2 years after the occurrence of the trauma. I have seen this throughout my naturopathic training and my subsequent years in private practice.

Normally, I use standard naturopathic interventions for the management of arthritis and elimination of joint inflammation and pain. These include dietary modification, nutrition supplements, rest, hydrotherapy, and exposure to sunlight, fresh air and gentle exercises. Also important in naturopathic counseling is the development of a proper mental attitude. In this last aspect of counseling, I have always been somewhat deficient. I would instruct my clients to replace negative thoughts with positive ones and encourage them not to dwell upon the traumas of the past. These strategies were, at best, ineffectual.

Prior to learning Thought Field Therapy, when working with an arthritis client I could completely eliminate most pain within six months to two years, depending upon the severity of their condition and how diligently a person followed the holistic health and nutrition program that I would design.

As for helping to relieve the traumatic experience that caused the onset of arthritis, frankly, I was at a total loss.

Thankfully, with TFT, I am now able to alleviate pain and help collapse the painful aftereffects of past traumatic experiences quickly and easily.

One example is "Pauline," a client of mine who, at 35 years of age, developed arthritic symptoms (including pain and a limited range of motion) in her neck and upper back as an aftereffect of a road accident. She was driving her car when she skidded on an ice patch, lost control and hit another car—injuring a young child who was a passenger (thankfully, not critically).

Pauline was treated at the scene of the accident using standard emergency procedures, such as immobilization with a cervical collar and backboard to prevent further injury. After hospitalization and rehabilitation, she was shown to suffer no additional pain and could move and walk normally.

One year following the accident, however, she began to develop pain and limited mobility of her neck and upper back again—the areas of her body that were previously deemed "healed." These symptoms worsened as time progressed, prompting her to seek medical attention. X-rays and medical assessment revealed no medical reason for the pain she was experiencing.

While interviewing Pauline regarding the cause of her present problem, I discovered she had been involved in a road accident, and felt guilty over causing the accident that injured the little girl, even though the child was not critically nor permanently injured.

Prior to TFT, my "treatment" of this individual would have addressed the physical aspects of her problem (neck pain and immobility) using the components of Traditional Naturopathy. While this would have helped ease the problem after several months (possibly), my level of training at the time would have made dealing with the psychological trauma and guilt almost impossible without a referral to an appropriate practitioner.

With TFT training, I was able to address the problems of trauma and guilt that I could not have addressed previously.

When I asked her to think about the accident, her SUD level became an immediate "10" and she began to cry. After calming her down, I diagnosed a unique TFT sequence for her and, by using it, brought her distress from a "10" to a "2" after only one treatment. A floor-to-ceiling eye roll brought her down to a "1."

She was amazed!

But *what amazed me* was that her chronic pain and immobility (which had always fluctuated between an "8" and a "10" on the SUD scale) immediately dropped to a "6" with no other treatment being done.

Lastly, I treated her for her guilty feeling over causing the accident and this distress was easily reduced. Her progress has been solid for the past six months, and thanks to TFT, she has been pain-free, guilt-free, and leading a generally happy and productive life.

Traditional Naturopaths are practitioners who help people to help themselves prevent pre-mature aging, restore general health and prevent illness using strategies which do not depend upon drugs or surgery (except in the most extreme of cases).

Using traditional methods, I got accustomed to seeing positive health benefits occur for my clients only after months or even years of effort. Thanks to TFT, the months have literally been reduced to minutes. My clients and I could not be happier with TFT!

—*Robert S. Harris*

* * *

Whenever we do live seminars to teach the TFT tapping sequences to everyday people, we use a doll to show the power of energy shared between two or more human beings. The doll, designed to sing whenever a child touches the metal disc embedded in its fabric palm, clearly demonstrates that electrical (and therefore healing) energy flows from one human being to another when they touch. As seminar attendees form a circle and clasp hands, the last person clasps the doll's palm—causing her to sing, showing that energy is flowing around the circle.

Just as energy can pass directly through a group of people in this demonstration—so, too, can energy pass through a group of people all focused energetically on tapping for a specific purpose.

We're reminded of the study where 4,000 people meditated and otherwise focused for 53 days on lowering crime in Washington, DC—the "murder capital of America." Miraculously, violent crime went down by more than 23%—a phenomenon that law enforcement officials said was so rare that it could happen only during the fiercest of winter storms when criminals were off the streets.

The study illustrates that energy can also be *passed through thought* from one person to another. In a further step, author Lynne McTaggart in her book, *The Intention Experiment,* documents both the transfer of energy and the transfer of intent. We demonstrate this through team tapping—a technique we'll discover in this next story.

 ## "Team Tapping" Leads to Enhanced Results

Imagine sleeping only three hours a night because of pain—or suffering from depression that limits your work, affects your marriage, and impacts your social and recreational functioning. Imagine living with pain from the top of your head all the way down to your toes—with the most intense pain in your head, abdomen, throat, arms and legs.

Such was the life that a female client of mine, "Nancy," suffered through.

A victim of intractable pain for more than a decade as a result of a medical procedure that went awry, Nancy rated her pain a "10" on the SUD scale *(subjective units of distress)*. Not only that, but she also had a prior trauma from a motor vehicle accident some 20 years earlier—which resulted in a coma and brain injury.

Clearly, she was suffering from Post-Traumatic Stress Disorder. And over the years, she had also been diagnosed with Chronic Regional Pain Syndrome (CRPS), Traumatic Brain Injury, and sensory peripheral neuropathy·. Medical evaluations diagnosed mild degeneration and bulge of her spinal discs, along with numerous liver cysts.

Of course, she had tried everything to ease the pain. From anesthetic blocks to steroid injections, heat, ice, acupuncture, massage, physical therapy, yoga, meditation, imagery, relaxation exercises, stretching, ultrasound, aquatherapy, traction, distraction (VAX-D), trigger point injections, prayer, and hypnosis. Her medicine cabinet was a revolving door of prescription drugs— Oxycontin, Tegretol, Neurontin, Cymbalta, Lyrica, Provigil, Kepra, fentanyl, methadone, phenergan, Ambien, and Actiq. She had been on narcotics, opiates, antidepressants, anti-inflammatory and sleeping medications.

Not surprisingly, she had reacted badly to many of these drugs—including reactions to sulfa meds, triptane, Celebrex, PCN, Stadol, Vioxx, Zomig, Vicodin, Tylenol with codeine and Bextra.

She reported suffering from vertigo. She had difficulty swallowing. She frequently had shortness of breath and tightness in her chest. Add to her suffering gastrointestinal problems, constipation, urinary hesitancy, intolerance to cold, difficulty concentrating, irritability, memory difficulties, mood swings, sleep disturbances, and night sweats—and it's easy to see why this client said she experienced "dead days" in which she could not function at all.

The worst part of her condition was that she was getting no noticeable result with any of these interventions and treatments.

Her first substantive relief was with Thought Field Therapy when, to her amazement, she dropped from 10 to 7 on the SUD scale with TFT sequences for trauma, pain, anger, frustration and stress. She did TFT treatments at home to manage the pain, but

---

* A painful condition characterized by burning, tingling or aching in the toes and soles of the feet which spreads to the ankles, knees and occasionally the hands and fingertips.

reported that she had even more profound effects tapping in my office—falling to as low as a "4" on the SUD scale.

This effect of me tapping along with Nancy got me thinking.

I remembered a TFT technique that our volunteer practitioner team had developed when treating the most severely pained genocide survivors in Rwanda in 2008. We actually enhanced the power of TFT by having additional practitioners tap together with the treating practitioner. We discovered this technique quite by accident when the newly trained Rwandan practitioners started tapping spontaneously after finishing the TFT treatments they were working on. They simply moved across the room to lend assistance and support to those who were still working.

I shared this story with Nancy and her husband who raised the question about what else could be done to enhance her results—since at this point they had stopped searching for other alternatives as new medical interventions either did nothing to ease her pain, or worse, aggravated her symptoms.

At first, we discussed having her husband join her in tapping out the TFT sequences—while we quickly recruited other TFT practitioners who might be willing to help in this trial of group support enhancement of TFT effects. Four TFT practitioners volunteered, and we met together for a group trial of TFT.

As Nancy, her husband, I and the four other TFT practitioners sat in a circle and started tapping on ourselves in unison, we witnessed Nancy experiencing a profound shift. The color in her face changed, and her posture shifted. She reported "a wave of release" and tears ran down her face. She is generally not an emotional person, and she and her husband shared how unusual it was for her to feel and express such strong emotions.

She said incredulously that her SUD had gone down to 2, which she had not imagined would be possible. She reported feeling the "blending" of energy throughout her entire body. She said it was the "best rush" she's ever felt, and moreover, said she had not felt that good or happy in a decade. The effects lasted for an hour, and her pain level remained at 4-5 until the middle of the next day. Interestingly, she also reported not having a "dead day" since the group intervention. On a follow-up group session, her original pain went to SUD 0. TFT has helped her better manage the pain and has enabled her to function more effectively.

To further her success, Nancy established a virtual team at home with her family members in another state, her husband and herself working together on Skype with videos of the treatment sequences playing simultaneously. Nancy reports that not only does she get deeper and longer lasting results than when she does the treatments alone, but that her virtual team members also report that they feel more relaxed, and are sleeping better, too!

—Caroline E. Sakai, PhD

*   *   *

As the founders of Thought Field Therapy, we are constantly improving and enhancing the TFT protocols to bring about faster and more effective relief. Not surprisingly, with a 30-year track record of healing and especially pain relief, TFT has captured the attention of mainstream medical personnel—many of whom have themselves benefited from TFT treatment.

Our next story is no exception. In fact, the nurse featured in the next few pages had tried every traditionally prescribed procedure and therapy for pain (including a few home remedies), yet nothing worked until a friend spent a few minutes treating her with TFT.

Forensic Nurse Solves Pain That Won't Go Away

As we dashed into the hotel lobby, shivering from the freezing wind of a chilly Denver night, my friend and I looked at each other and laughed—remembering the great day we had had.

We were conference presenters together and followed the morning's proceedings with a calming afternoon of wine, massage, tea and friendship—after briefly visiting a reception for speakers at the conference.

I am a psychologist and TFT practitioner in Los Angeles, and my friend is a forensic nurse with more than 20 years in the medical field.

As we took off our coats, she sighed and revealed, "This cold really makes that pain in my arm hurt like a son of a gun."

Never having heard her mention it before, I asked, "What pain?"

And with that innocent question began one of the most extraordinary TFT treatment sessions of my career.

As it turns out, my friend had quietly lived with moderate to severe chronic pain for nearly 10 years. While studying for her Advanced Cardiac Life Support certificate as a recovery room and short stay nurse, she had taken a break and stretched her arms into the air. As her chair unexpectedly flipped backwards, she instinctively extended her right arm to break her fall. Painfully, her right shoulder dislocated, then snapped back into place sending an immediate sensation of electric "nerve like" pain shooting through her arm. It made her hand feel fat, she said, and her entire arm hummed—from her brachial plexus to her elbow to her palm.

For 10 years, that feeling of electrical "zinging" down her arm was present and never went away.

After two surgeries, nine years of physical therapy, a trip to a specialist out of state, eight years of acupuncture, nine years of Pilates, and seven years of massage—plus ongoing home pain management made up of Oxycontin, Vicodin, Flexeril, pain gel, ice, heat and more massages than she could count, my friend still lived each day with the same searing electrical pain running down her arm.

"I'd like to try something with you for that pain," I said.

And while she went along with what I suggested, I could tell that the cynical portion of her very medical-model brain was trying not to laugh out loud. She told me later she thought the pain would never respond to anything—after everything that she had tried already.

Still, desperate for anything that might improve her condition, she watched carefully as I demonstrated the TFT sequence for pain relief.

Her physical pain was almost unbearable—an "8" on the SUD scale because of the cold weather, she said. Submissively tapping herself on the back of her hand and collarbone without regard or thought that TFT was going to work, my friend unexpectedly said to me, "Wow, was I wrong."

The pain in her arm was gone!

Within minutes, she no longer had the constant "nerve pain" in her hand, elbow and shoulder. Her hand no longer felt clumsy and fat. Her fingers, though still a bit swollen, began to take on the same color as her other hand. And while she still anticipated pain when she raised her arm or placed her hand in cold water, actually lifting her arm and dousing her hand caused her no pain whatsoever. She could in fact raise her arm!

Even days later, the pain did not come back. And that was with five minutes of TFT treatment. For the first time, she could look forward to physical activity.

Plus, she used TFT to relieve other conditions that paled when compared to the overarching pain. She wrote me later to say that she was working on lowering her blood pressure, and that by using the tapping therapy, she treated herself for pain and arthritis in her toes. She even healed tinnitus in her ear, she wrote.

While she's still not sure exactly how TFT works, she's convinced it works. "I am not sure how or why," she wrote, "but it does. It simply does."

—Nora J. Baladerian, PhD

* * *

The beauty of Thought Field Therapy is the speed with which it relieves pain. From a single tapping sequence which takes just a few minutes, to multiple tapping sequences which some people require, TFT is effective and fast.

Of course, pain specialists know that the ache and throbbing of chronic pain can actually inhibit healing of some injuries. However, once TFT removes the pain, healing can happen faster and with better results.

In this next story of a wedding celebration which could have ended in disaster, an important guest is out of bed and back in action within minutes of her TFT treatment.

How TFT Prevented a Wedding Day Disaster

I attended an out-of-town wedding in Atlanta, and while at the cocktail party, I noted that a dear friend—who I knew had flown in for the wedding—was not in attendance. When I made inquiries, I was told that the pain from her recent hip injury was so "out of control" that it had confined her to bed, so she wouldn't be attending the cocktail party or dinner that evening.

When I went up to her room to visit and see what I could do for her, sure enough "Eileen" was lying in bed with a forced smile on her face, breathing shallowly.

She told me the pain medicine she was on wasn't helping, but that she didn't want to go the narcotic route. She knew that I had trained in EFT, so she asked me about it. I then told her about Thought Field Therapy and how I felt I had learned some very valuable additional techniques that could help her.

She was more than happy to try anything at that point. Her SUD level was a "10+" for pain. I used the TFT sequence for trauma first because she was very upset and devastated by her injury. In fact, her level of upset was equal to the pain—also a "10." She is a fitness instructor and yoga teacher who took her new advanced certification to an extreme and tore her hip cartilage.

With the trauma sequence, her SUD dropped to an 8, and then 5.

She also told me she was very embarrassed that this had happened to her and that she should have known better. Using the tapping sequence for embarrassment did the trick—it brought her upset down to a "1."

Finally ready to deal with her pain, I used the TFT treatment sequence which brought her pain down to a "7." After another round, it dropped to a "5." I treated her for *psychological reversal* and repeated the pain sequence—this time asking her to focus on the color of the pain, as well as on whether the pain was sharp or dull in nature. Her SUD level dropped to a "1."

By this time my husband was calling to tell me the guests were being seated for dinner, so I needed to go down to the ballroom. Fifteen minutes later my friend joined us saying that "the TFT stuff really works!"

—*Marysue Hansell*

* * *

Many TFT practitioners combine the tapping techniques and diagnostic procedures with other methods they use in their current work. In this next story from a Clinical Reflexologist, the practitioner sees the link between TFT, pain treatment, and her own work.

 Reflexology and Thought Field Therapy

I have been working as a Clinical Reflexologist· for nine years which involves using advanced techniques and tailoring each treatment to the patient's current needs.

This also means I am open to new methods.

I first heard of TFT when I was invited to an Introduction to TFT conducted by Roger and Joanne Callahan. After reading more about it, I decided to attend as I had seen the tapping techniques used by a Kinesiologist who I knew got results with them.

I was fascinated by what I saw at this course and began to experiment a little with the sequences. I also met a woman who practices both Reflexology and TFT who told me that she had gotten excellent results by following Reflexology treatments with TFT.

This got me thinking about the relationship that might be made between TFT and Reflexology.

∗ A Clinical Reflexologist works to relieve pain by massaging predefined pressure points on the feet and hands which is thought to stimulate the body's organs and glands via the nervous system.

Beginning with some of my longtime Reflexology patients, I began to follow-up Reflexology with a TFT treatment. One of my patients was suffering with unexplained pain in her thigh. I remembered from my training that we could directly tap on problem areas for psychological reversal·, and I wondered if it would work through the reflex point. During the patient's next Reflexology treatment, I tapped for reversal whilst touching the associated reflex point for the thigh—her problem area.

She told me later that when I had "shaken her foot," which must have been how the indirect tapping had felt to her, that she had had a moment of nausea, after which the pain diminished considerably.

It is now several months after that treatment and the pain has totally disappeared other than some discomfort when she stands for long periods of time—and this without her pursuing any additional treatment or at-home remedies which I suggested. All she does is the standard tapping throughout the day to remove minor agitations.

Another Reflexology patient has long-term problems with her neck, which eventually flared up into muscle spasms. I treated the condition with Reflexology, but recommended that she tap every day on the reflex points for the neck—and so far she is improving well.

—*Rita New, MBRCP*

* * *

Of course, while it is certainly recommended that you work with a TFT practitioner to relieve pain, the reality is that it isn't always necessary. In this final story about using TFT for pain relief, an Australian man who was simply attending a seminar gets relief by reading *Tapping the Healer Within* (Roger's original book about TFT) and following the tapping sequence for pain.

---

* Psychological reversal (or "PR") is a blockage or reversal of the energy flows in your body's energy pathways. It keeps all kinds of treatments from working as well as they should. PR can be easily eliminated by tapping midway on the outside edge of your hand prior to using other tapping sequences for your illness or disorder. TFT practitioners always test for PR prior to TFT treatment.

Three Minutes + A Book = Pain Relief

By the end of the first day of a TFT training in Perth, Western Australia, I could really relate to all the traumas that people were suffering from. Not only that, but I could also see that TFT was working on that day.

We were given some homework to do that night in preparation for the next day's session. And, as I was sitting in my hotel room reading the book, *Tapping the Healer Within,* I remembered that I had asked our workshop instructor, Eugene Piccinotti, about the tapping sequences for pain.

Having assured me that he would cover it the next day, I sat in bed reading the book and found the procedure for pain. The reason I wanted to know about this was that I had long suffered pain in both my feet due to collapsed arches—and I could not get relief from it. So I studied the chapter about relieving pain with TFT, and—doing the sequence as shown in the book—within about three minutes, I got out of bed and walked around the hotel room.

The pain in my feet had gone.

It has not returned either and I now play golf and lawn bowling pain-free. I stood up in front of the class at the workshop the next day and broke down when I told them of my experience. It made me a true believer in TFT.

—Robert K. Allen

* * *

As the story above undeniably shows, TFT is simple and works whether the "patient" is fully trained in the tapping techniques or even agrees that they will work. As the next story shows, no one is too young to get pain relief using TFT.

Even Babies Can Overcome Pain With TFT

Recently I was treating a patient for smoking. She had brought her five-month old granddaughter "Rebecca" with her to my office.

While my patient was eager to proceed with treatment, poor Rebecca was not. The baby was teething and in a great deal of discomfort. She cried, moaned, thrashed and was generally unhappy.

It would have been heartless and fruitless to continue our work while Rebecca suffered. I considered my treatment options. Reframing was clearly out of the question, as was trance induction, reinforcement and empathizing—all due to the fact that I still had not yet mastered "baby language."

I thought, however, that TFT might be helpful.

I asked my patient if I could tap out the pain sequence on Rebecca. Since she was familiar with TFT, she readily agreed.

The results were astounding.

Within 30 seconds, Rebecca progressed from being completely miserable to cooing contentedly, and we could proceed with her grandmother's treatment (along with an occasional "booster" for Rebecca). This single incident was so satisfying that it alone could have justified my investment in becoming a TFT practitioner.

—*Mark Matloff, PhD*

* * *

Babies are easy to work with using the TFT tapping sequences because, when they hurt, they are laser-beam focused on their pain. The SUD rating is always a "10" with a baby. Nothing is right with the world, and no amount of cuddling, cooing or bribery will ease the ache.

And whether you tap directly on the infant, as the next story will show, or whether you use the surrogate technique as others in this book have done, TFT can bring about near-instantaneous relief for infant pain.

One of Those "Cantankerous" Moods

Thought Field Therapy so quickly helped my 11-month-old granddaughter that it wiped away any lingering doubts I may have had that TFT was too good to be true. My granddaughter was sick, and my daughter—who is a middle-school teacher—had a meeting the next day she simply could not miss. Uncomfortable with the idea of taking my sick granddaughter to daycare, she asked if I would babysit the next day.

When they arrived the next morning, my granddaughter wasn't as ill as I expected. She was a bit cranky, but things were fine until about 11:00 when she apparently spiked a fever and began to cry. The crying was not just normal fussing, but the kind of heart-rending crying that says, *Everything is wrong with the world and I hurt.*

She was in one of those cantankerous moods when the constant fussing means, *Pick me up. Put me down. I want a bottle,* only to knock it away when you hand it to her.

After about 25 minutes of this agonized crying, I was beginning to feel completely inadequate and getting more than a little frustrated about what to do. It occurred to me that TFT had been used with young children and that I might be able to try the tapping sequences with her since she was certainly focused on where she was hurting.

I began tapping on her eyebrow which she did not like at all. Then, I tapped the spot underneath the eyes as she struggled and fought me. But I noticed as I went to tap the collarbone, for the first time, she began to look at me in a funny way. As I moved to her fingers, her crying slowed, then stopped when I tapped her collarbone again. But the one thing that surprised me more than anything was that she held out her little finger to me as I reached for her hand in order for me to tap the last of the series.

For the rest of the day, things were pretty good. As soon as she began to fuss a little, about 10 seconds later the crying would stop. It would just sort of dissipate.

That was a wonderful thing to have happen. My wife pointed out something else that has been rather nice. Since that time, whenever my daughter and her family come to visit, my granddaughter seems to think that Grandpa is a really special person and spends a lot of her time with me. TFT is pretty wonderful in a whole bunch of ways.

—*Robert Paige, LCSW*

Tapping Away Physical Pain

You'll find videos that step you through the complete tapping sequence for eliminating physical pain at our website:

www.rogercallahan.com/pathways

10 Chapter Ten:
Tapping Away Depression, Self-Harm and Suicidal Thoughts

Our complicated world creates more depression, sadness and hopelessness than most people realize. The mounting responsibilities we face, the realization that we can't do it all, losing someone we love, our identity fading away due to a career downturn or business loss—all these situations can cause feelings of depression and even suicidal thoughts. Not only that, but changes in our brain chemistry due to poor nutrition, aging, hormone imbalances and other factors can also cause depression.

Twice as frequent in woman than in men, depression can lead to difficulty in concentrating, fatigue, withdrawal from family and friends, and the loss of interest in formerly pleasurable activities.

When depression or suicidal thoughts make a formerly enjoyable life seem impossible to enjoy now, it's time to take action.

We've used Thought Field Therapy for nearly three decades to alleviate feelings of melancholy, hopelessness and despair. But while TFT can relieve the dark and foreboding feeling of depression, we recommend that *you also seek the care of a mental health professional* if you are depressed—even though you choose to use TFT as part of your treatment.

Why?

Because depression is a serious illness. It can lead to an increased risk of suicide. Make no mistake: Thoughts of suicide or talk of taking your own life is a medical and psychological emergency.

But this caveat should not add to your worry. In fact, the stories of success in this chapter should provide hope and help if you are suffering. Let's take a look:

By Far, the Most Common Illness

Studying at a traditional medical school—then later pursuing a practice in alternative medicine—has led me down a fascinating path over the last 38 years. I've been exposed to numerous therapies, philosophies, and ideas, plus a tremendous amount of new information.

Until recently, I was totally unfamiliar with Thought Field Therapy. Then I spent three days at a TFT Diagnostic Training Program and my medical world changed.

I've treated close to 50 patients using TFT—with symptoms ranging from depression (which is by far the most common malady) to phobias, stress, acute traumas and grief.

What I have experienced is amazing.

Not only do patients respond well to the TFT treatment emotionally, but their appearance changes as well. It's like a burden is lifted from their shoulders, and they become animated, happy, smiling and a few even dance around the room. The contrast is like night and day.

To be able to give to patients the tools to treat themselves is awesome, humbling, overwhelming and thrilling.

I look forward to using this diagnostic and treatment tool to improve my care of the challenging and difficult patients as I become more knowledgeable and more skilled. Thank you, Roger and Joanne Callahan!

—Arthur R. Davis, Jr., MD

* * *

General practitioners—that is, the family doctor—are often the first physician to encounter depression in a patient, simply because they see patients more often than specialists. Fortunately, the doctor in the story above is now able to use TFT as a first line of defense in halting the progress of depression.

Not only is this a time-saver (and potential life-saver) for the patient, but it immediately eliminates the even more depressing prospect of a long sequence of psychotherapy—an expensive, protracted and all-consuming process that often makes patients feel broken, fragile and powerless to manage their own recovery.

TFT, on the other hand, rapidly eliminates the depression and instead puts the patient in a stronger, more enthusiastic state—full of life and eagerly looking forward to the future.

In this next article adapted from our newsletter, *The Thought Field,* we detail the objective evidence that shows how TFT works with depression, and why it is superior in eliminating this illness.

 Eliminating Depression Improves Longevity, Too

In our work over the past 30 years, we've not only developed TFT as a therapy for all kinds of illnesses, but we've also studied one of the primary indicators of why some people live longer—and others don't.

It's called *heart rate variability*—a measure of the autonomic nervous system, the body's complicated network of nerve endings and electrical impulses that control involuntary functions such as heartbeat, digestion, perspiration, breathing and so on.

When researchers first discovered that heart rate variability, or HRV, was a good indicator of longevity and an even better measure of overall good health, we immediately began testing whether *tapping* could improve HRV and bring about an actual physiological change in the body's efficient functioning.

Our years of testing for changes using HRV tells us that tapping does indeed improve heart rate variability almost within minutes of TFT treatment.

For instance, while quitting smoking or working out at the gym for six months improve HRV by about 20%, a single treatment with TFT typically improves it by as much as 156%! This suggests that TFT is accomplishing something very deep, very powerful, and biologically restorative.

So what does all this have to do with depression?

Researchers believe that severe depression unfortunately causes physiological damage to the patient, and that—because of deep negative and permanent biological change—it's virtually impossible to improve heart rate variability. Alarmingly, Dr. Robert Carney and his fellow researchers at the Washington University School of Medicine said, "It is possible that heart rate and HRV never return to normal once there has been an episode of major depression."·

If this were correct, their pessimistic conclusion would be terrible news for anyone who ever suffered from depression. But when we test depressed people for HRV after treating them with Thought Field Therapy, we find unequivocally that not only does TFT *rapidly eliminate the depression,* but a single tapping session improves heart rate variability, too.

Imagine emerging from depression not only stronger mentally, but stronger physically, as well.

Not only that, but in those cases from our files of people who suffered from severe depression (and from whom we took an HRV reading prior to their tapping treatment), patients' heart rate variability improved by more than 150%. Such improvements are unprecedented. But in each case, the depression was completely eliminated with TFT—and the improvement was accomplished *with just one TFT session,* taking only minutes rather than weeks or months as other forms of therapy do.

Although this is not a detailed scientific study, these real-world results negate the pessimistic notion of permanent biological damage caused by depression. When depressed people are treated with TFT, not only is it possible to rapidly eliminate the depression, but it's also expected that overall health will improve, too.

—Roger J. Callahan, PhD

* * *

Giving a depressed person a new lease on life or even saving a patient from potential suicide is perhaps the most gratifying and rewarding work that our trained TFT practitioners do. Many of them—myself included—admit they were frustrated with

---

* Dr. Robert Carney and other Washington University physicians studied how cognitive behavioural therapy—or "talk therapy"—impacted depression. In many cases, after just 16 therapy sessions, the patients' physical health actually got worse.

their inability to reverse such a debilitating condition with traditional therapy.

In this next story of an emergency mental health crisis, a TFT practitioner talks a depressed and suicidal person through the tapping sequence in the hospital emergency room.

Averting the Second Tragedy of Suicide

"Maryanne" is a TFT miracle. She had lost her only child to a very tragic car accident, and—having struggled with alcoholism for most of her life—when her daughter was decapitated in the accident, Maryanne could not find relief. She had tried other types of therapy and treatment, but nothing helped.

Unexpectedly, I was called to the hospital emergency room where Maryanne was homicidal and suicidal. I had her tap out the TFT sequence for trauma and she was immediately relieved. She went from being unable to say her daughter's name to telling me the whole story. She no longer saw her daughter lying there without a head, but slowly began to see her lying asleep with the sun shinning through her hair.

The potential tragedy of suicide had been averted.

Then, four days after the violent events of September 11th, I called Maryanne to see how she was doing. As she answered the phone, I could hardly understand her. Clearly, she had been crying while watching the aftermath of the terrorist attacks unfold on television. She was unable to do anything. She thought she was going crazy.

Maryanne told me that her brother and nephew were working at the Pentagon, but had not been heard from. She had spoken with her sister and, after watching TV virtually non-stop for four days, was totally out of control. She was angry at God and the world for not taking her life instead. She hadn't slept since the attacks.

I asked her if she remembered the tapping sequence we did at the hospital and whether she would allow me to walk her through it over the phone. She agreed to try and we started tapping. Immediately, I noticed a change in her voice. I further treated her for anger—after which the bitter emotions and physical distress simply left her. She was calm and at peace.

As she looked at the television, a news program re-ran the footage of planes flying into the World Trade Center, but Maryanne felt no anxiety. I suggested that she not watch the news more than 10 to 15 minutes an hour—and to get some sleep.

The next morning when I called, though she was sad about the events, she said she was doing fine. She had finally been able to take care of her own needs—which she had not done for the past four days. She had slept the night through without the terrible nightmares that had kept her wakeful for nearly 96 hours.

Since that day, I've talked to her again, and she has been doing fine—now a true believer in TFT.

—James C. McAninch

* * *

Severe depression and violent suicidal episodes aren't the only kind of depression that affects everyday people. Sometimes it's simple melancholy, that feeling of being "down" without one's usual zest for life. In this next story of a vibrant and successful woman who falls into mild depression, we see many of the symptoms that millions of people experience every day—along with a successful outcome using TFT.

 ### Reviving a "Broken Spirit"

"Beverly," a beautiful 47-year old client with whom I've worked on several psychological issues, simply felt stuck. She was "down" and had none of her normal motivation or zest for life. She was deeply disturbed by the fact that I was unable to provide any sensible explanations or "causes" for her distress by using our usual therapeutic modalities.

Generally an energized, bright, and vivacious super-achiever, for the previous three weeks Beverly had suffered from a vague and stubbornly undefinable "broken spirit." She was avoiding many of her normally desirable activities, including a much-anticipated vacation and open communication with her husband, which she had worked so diligently to achieve.

Beverly felt as if she were falling into an abyss, with no purpose or meaning in her life. I tried numerous ways of confronting and diagnosing her dilemma, using all of the standard TFT algorithms for anxiety, depression, trauma and more. Using TFT diagnostic procedures I was able to provide some temporary periods of relief lasting for several hours and an intermittent sense of feeling better. However, these treatments were not holding. There had to be more we could do. I was unable to find any toxins through TFT testing.

At this point, I also felt stuck! Then I called Dr. Callahan for help over the phone. Within 18 minutes, he and I were able to completely eliminate the problem of Beverly's "broken spirit"— with all disturbances gone. Her anxiety lifted, the light and sparkle returned to her eyes, and she suddenly felt life was "incredibly worth living." She was back to being her dynamic self.

The procedures were lengthy and complicated, and I would never have discovered all of the treatment points required in this case without Roger. Additionally, he was able to discover one toxin—coffee. After agreeing to give it up, she has been happy, full of life and off of coffee for the past two weeks.

—*Mona A. Coates*

* * *

Occasionally depression, melancholy, hopelessness and despair deteriorate into something far worse—self-inflicted harm to one's own body. In such cases, immediate psychiatric treatment and intervention is crucial.

In this next story of a young woman whose lifelong battle with multiple-personality disorder brings her to the crisis point, TFT is able to stop the self-harm, eliminate the self-hatred and relieve the suffering.

The Tragedy of Self-Harm

My personal experience with TFT was so powerful that it feels important to share it with others.

My therapist began using TFT on me to help get me through painful memories, traumas and places where I felt "stuck" in my life. In addition to how incredibly it works, one of the best aspects of this therapy for me is that I do not have to go through and get through the painful emotional and physical distress of having to "re-live" the specific memory or trauma.

Using TFT, my therapist has helped me through a number of ugly memories as well as some periods of feeling really terrible about myself—to the extent of wanting to actually cause physical harm to myself. But I have come very far with TFT. In fact, some of these past negative, and very traumatic, experiences were so thoroughly resolved that I only remember them now when someone outside of myself brings them up. They simply don't bother me anymore!

There are two particularly amazing TFT healing experiences I've had that I would like to share.

First is from a time when I was overwhelmed by intense feelings of confusion and self-hatred. These feelings got so bad at the time that I was struggling hourly not to hurt myself. I could barely function. Then my therapist worked through the TFT routines with me and the results were incredible! In just one session of TFT, those intense feelings of self-hatred disappeared. My thoughts changed from, *I HATE myself, I want to slice myself up*—to *I don't hate myself, why on earth would I want to hate myself, there's no reason for that.* By the time we were done I felt wonderful. I felt balanced and at ease, which was a complete turnaround from how I felt when I entered into the session.

The effects have remained stable for some time now. Not for a single moment since the treatment have I been haunted by feelings and thoughts of intense hatred or destructiveness, thoughts and feelings that had consumed me for years before the treatment. I even noticed that young children respond differently to me now, perhaps sensing how at peace I am with myself.

In another amazing experience I had with TFT, I learned that while I can't change the things that I have done, I now know that I can move past the abusive cycles I would get into in the past, and that I can and will heal. That makes all the difference in the world to me. And, I haven't had a single relapse of any issues we've covered. That's the highest success rate I've had in over five years of therapy. I'm here to say that TFT has really worked for me and made a huge difference in my life.

In contrast to other treatments that I've had, I find that TFT treatments instantly elevate my mood and make me feel like a new person, and that I am significantly more energetic and productive—which is a long way away from the *'barely able to move or think'* feeling I've had after other therapy sessions.

I have also found TFT useful in treating my headaches and sleep disturbances. I use a simple treatment sequence taught to me by my therapist. They work as well as any medication I've tried, sometimes even better! TFT has had a profound and long lasting affect on my life.

—*Elizabeth Neiderer/John H. Diepold, Fr, PhD*

Tapping Away Depression, Self-Harm And Suicidal Thoughts

You'll find videos that step you through the complete tapping sequences for relieving depression at our website:

www.rogercallahan.com/pathways

11

Chapter Eleven:
Halting Addictions with
Thought Field Therapy

Over the years, we've seen more and more addiction patients in our practice. And while entire industries have been built around helping addicts to overcome their addictions, we've repeatedly confirmed through diagnosis of patients that addiction is simply a response to anxiety and stress.

Remove the anxiety and stress, and the addiction will disappear. And whether it's an addiction to drugs, nicotine, food or an activity—doesn't matter. All addictions are, in fact, a desperate attempt by the patient to deal with overwhelming anxiety and stress.

The desire to find comfort and peace by smoking, eating, inhaling—or whatever method—is what we call the addictive urge. Unfortunately, these urges can be so powerful that even patients who experience heart attacks, diabetes, emphysema, relationship breakdowns, job loss, financial ruin and criminal convictions will still smoke, overeat, abuse drugs or drink excessively.

In other words, they know their addiction is slowly killing them and ruining their life, but they give in repeatedly to the addictive urge. Tragically, however, once the brief period of comfort or the fleeting "high" wears off, the stress and anxiety still remains. That's where Thought Field Therapy can stop the cycle of addiction. In this first story, we get a first-hand report on exactly how TFT works to address addiction.

 "Has This Therapist Lost His Marbles?"

About four years ago, I read an article in a national newsletter describing a treatment for neutralizing addictive urges. The author, a psychologist, suggested that addiction is essentially an anxiety disorder, and that an addicted person attempts to mask the anxiety by using a substance. While I readily concurred with the author based on my own 21 years of working with addiction, I had a difficult time swallowing the treatment procedure.

He recommended that therapists have their patients pay attention to their addictive urge while tapping on various body points! I remember thinking at the time that the therapist had most likely lost his marbles, and rapidly shoved the article aside.

Months later I was treating a person who was dependent on opioids·. During one of our sessions she evidenced a strong urge, becoming quite pale and shaky after discussing her affinity for the drug. I attempted to help settle the urge by using a cognitive ("talk therapy") technique known as Rational Emotive Imagery (REI). While we were able to reduce the craving somewhat, the intensity returned moments later.

Then I recalled the strange procedure I had read about.

At first I was a little embarrassed to suggest it to my client, but then I figured we had nothing to lose. I simply told her that there was another technique that might help, although I could not promise that it would. I pointed out that it did not seem likely to do any harm, but that it might also do nothing at all. Talk about setting the stage for positive expectations!

My client shrugged her shoulders and agreed to give it a try. We had reasoned at the time that if she had a means of settling addictive urges without using drugs, she would be more inclined to do so—which would only aid her recovery.

I asked her to tap under her eyes, then about four inches under her armpit, then finally under her collarbones. To my surprise, repeating this treatment several times brought the addictive urge down to a "4" on a scale of 0 to 10.

While we were unable to dissipate the urge any further, she wasn't able to intensify the urge either—even though I asked her to think about "how good it would feel" to give in to the urge. While I realized at the time that I had much more to learn about this mysterious tapping technique, needless to say both my client and I were quite impressed with its results.

---

* A synthetic narcotic, such as OxyContin or Vicodin, that acts like an opiate but is not derived from opium.

I couldn't even recall who wrote the article, but I was fairly sure that I had kept it. In desperation, I rummaged through huge stacks and files of papers at my office and at home. Eventually I found the newsletter. The article I sought was written by Dr. Roger J. Callahan of Indian Wells, California.

After reading the article again, I wondered if there might not be more to this method. I decided to give Dr. Callahan a call, and before long I was reviewing his materials and talking to him regularly. What a delight!

I had been looking for something new and exciting, something truly effective in helping people, and knew I had found it in Dr. Callahan's work. This was a whole new dimension in understanding and treating psychological problems. As a professional, I was inspired once again.

Shortly after contacting Dr. Callahan, I learned more about treating addictive urges. I saw my client with the opioid problem and treated her again with more detailed Thought Field Therapy procedures. By this time I understood more about treatment points, psychological reversal, and other aspects of TFT. My client and I were easily able to alleviate addictive urges within moments. Not only that, but she was equipped to treat herself at will.

Then one day she returned to the office for a session and I asked about her progress. She reported that she was still using drugs occasionally. Amazed, I questioned at first whether the "tapping technique" was helping.

Her response? "Oh, I don't use tapping all the time. It works!"

Suddenly, her reaction made sense. There is an obvious difference between addiction and addictive urge. Of course the addicted person wants to get rid of the urge; that's why he or she takes the drug. The drug alleviates the urge—which is really anxiety and other disturbing emotions coming to the surface.

But after the urge is removed, there is still something else present: The effects of the drug itself including the "high," the camaraderie, and the self sabotage—just to mention a few.

We've always known that addiction has many facets, but I had momentarily overlooked this point in my fervor to neutralize one of its components, the urge.

The beauty of TFT, however, is that it assists the therapist in mapping out the various components of an addiction, while providing a precise solution for alleviating each aspect of the addiction. Another benefit of TFT is that, as each aspect of a addiction is resolved, the underlying layers of the addiction present themselves for treatment in logical order. Just like a cafeteria tray dispenser, after you take the top tray from the stack, the next tray pops right up. TFT makes treating addiction as simple as can be.

—*Fred P. Gallo, PhD*

* * *

While addictions almost always control a person's life, in the end they can easily be rendered powerless. Why? Because addictions are really just a stress response to underlying anxiety, as we have seen time and again in our practice.

In this next story, longtime TFT practitioner Dr. Robert Bray explains the emotional reasons behind addiction, and makes the case that—left untreated—such emotional responses, usually to stress or a past traumatic experience can sometimes drive a person to end their own life. TFT can help eliminate the harmful emotions and overwhelming feelings that one is powerless to manage life's situations or live in a worthwhile way.

 ## The Hopelessness That Leads to Self-Destruction

Sometimes people experience such terrible events that they can't be expected to recover quickly or easily. When what has happened feels so scary that we cannot look at it long enough to understand what happened or make sense of its aftereffects, we may struggle not only with the desire not to face this trauma— but also with feeling hopeless and isolated.

If you are currently facing these conditions, be aware that you are at risk for addictions and suicidal behavior.

Let's look at addictions first. To end the discomfort of an incomplete recovery process and to manage the overwhelming feelings of being unable to process your current condition or what happened to you, people often turn to alcohol or other drugs to medicate the pain or to function throughout the day. Other high-risk behaviors such as fighting, speeding in cars, or having unsafe sex accomplish the same goal as alcohol and drug abuse. They distract you from the sensations and thoughts that overwhelm you and make you uncomfortable.

Oftentimes using Thought Field Therapy to eliminate the upset feelings eliminates the need for self-medicating—and stops the dangerous behavior. Sometimes, if a habit has formed and become strongly entrenched, to heal completely you will have to directly treat the urge to use drugs or behaviors.

Using TFT to relieve the underlying anxiety that drives these behaviors returns you to a safer lifestyle.

As for suicidal behavior and thoughts, these often accompany the feelings of hopelessness and isolation that follow traumatic experiences. Overwhelming emotions often convince trauma victims that they cannot manage to live a worthwhile life—and these emotions can actually drive one to believe they'll be better off dead than continuing in their current state.

This condition is worsened by feelings that no one understands you, that you are powerless, that your symptoms will never improve, that no one exists who can help you or who even cares about your condition. When these overwhelming feelings emerge, trauma victims find themselves at high risk for self-destruction.

While open wounds left by traumatic experiences can make anyone feel alone, Thought Field Therapy helps heal those wounds, thus curing the feeling of isolation. By removing desperate feelings, tapping helps you become more connected to other people and less inclined to hurt yourself or commit suicide. The reason for this is simple: hopelessness and isolation together form a deadly combination. In most people's lives, a connection to loved ones, family, and community increases the ability to endure horrible conditions and terrible pain. We can stand more pain and upset when we are connected to others, and hope always lives through that connection. Hope and love keep us alive.

Isolation, on the other hand, makes us wither.

If you are thinking or acting in self-destructive ways, keep reaching out to other people and begin using Thought Field Therapy immediately. Seek out peer help and, more importantly, professional help. Somewhere, someone will understand and accept you as you are.

There is hope for ending your unlivable conditions and for connecting to other people.

—*Robert L. Bray, PhD*
LCSW, CTS

* * *

Of course, some addictions are far less serious than drugs or reckless behavior. Smoking is one of these—but just like other addictions, it can control a person's life in the near-term and limit their ability to enjoy a healthful life in the long-term.

Can giving up cigarettes really be as simple as a few taps? Take a look at the next story to see how easy it can be with TFT.

"It's So Simple, It Can't Work..."

Last week I had a client, age 56, who had been smoking two packs of cigarettes a day for 42 years. He was in a near panic since nothing he had tried had helped him stop smoking. From hypnosis to the patch—nothing met with success.

I showed him the video about TFT and how it works to eliminate the smoking habit. Once he felt comfortable about trying "tapping," we began our session. I led him through the standard TFT treatment for addiction—and he completed the tapping sequence in about three minutes.

By that point, he no longer had the craving for cigarettes and couldn't summon up a craving even after trying. He let out a big sigh and, with tears in his eyes, said he could not get the craving to return.

He looked at me and said, "I haven't felt this good since I was a young man!"

He couldn't believe that a technique this simple could work. Yet he's doing great and not smoking. Not bad for a three-minute treatment!

—*Kenneth G. Kuchar-Haas*

* * *

When we think of addictions, drugs, cigarettes and alcohol usually come to mind. But therapists have long known that patients can become addicted to specific habits and behaviors, too. When repeated patterns of behavior get in the way of a normal life, psychologists call that Obsessive Compulsive Disorder. When patients constantly have unwanted thoughts, that's an obsession. Repeating certain behaviors is a compulsion.

Of course, most clients know their actions make no sense, but they're powerless to ignore the thoughts or stop the behaviors.

In our practice, we approach Obsessive Compulsive Disorder as an addiction to a specific behavior—a distressing condition which causes the person to constantly repeat the same action over and over, sometimes as many as 100 or more times a day.

In this next story from a TFT practitioner who has had success in treating OCD, we get a glimpse not only of how OCD can consume a patient's life, but also of how TFT can return them to a life free of compulsive, addictive behavior.

Is There Such a Thing As a Behavioral Addiction?

Obsessive Compulsive Disorder affects 1 in 50 people. It can destroy lives and ruin marriages. And some sufferers have even been known to commit suicide to escape the distress of constantly repeating the same obsessive behavior—powerless to stop themselves.

Unfortunately, conventional medical treatment is of little value with OCD. Drugs merely calm the symptoms, while cognitive behavior therapy ("talk therapy") is virtually useless. Indeed many psychologists regard OCD as an "incurable" condition.

Recently I treated a patient with OCD using advanced TFT procedures. What was astonishing about this case was not the fact that a cure was obtained (which is often the case with TFT), but that the treatment time was very short—measured in mere minutes.

A 57-year-old woman contacted me after hearing me talk about TFT on a BBC Radio show. She had suffered from OCD since the age of eight—causing her to check things excessively and to count numbers repeatedly.

Her initial SUD (*subjective units of distress*) was a "10." She was also found to have a few toxins—namely wheat, tomatoes, vinegar and chocolate.

At a follow-up appointment a week later she reported that she had had no recurrence of her symptoms since the initial treatment. Her SUD was 1 and she found it hard to believe that she was now cured after years of unsuccessful conventional therapy.

One factor that contributed to this very successful outcome was that the client agreed to avoid all toxins totally. The short treatment time of just a few minutes was astonishing, even by the standards of TFT. While Thought Field Therapy is often called the "Five Minute Phobia Cure," in this instance it was also the Five Minute OCD Cure!

—Dr. Colin Barron

* * *

Ancient scholars and people in positions of spiritual leadership have long preached about the toll that repeated bad behavior takes on a person's life. In fact, they've written about it almost as long as language has been available to discuss it.

In this next perspective from a modern-day scholar and TFT practitioner, we see stress release and spiritual renewal combine with TFT. Father Luis Jorge González is a professor at the Carmelite College in Rome and even contributed a chapter about TFT in a book on spiritual therapy published by the Vatican.

The Seven Deadly Addictions

In both the Catholic Church and the Orthodox Church, there are people who suffer what church leaders and Christian writers from the 2nd through 12th Centuries have called "sicknesses of the soul." Others call these sicknesses by their more common name, *The Seven Deadly Sins*: Pride, gluttony, greed, lust, anger, envy, and sloth.

But, in my opinion, these vices are not necessarily sins. As we've come to consider them in modern times, they are sicknesses of the mind, disordered emotions and behavioral addictions. Therefore, they need to be addressed not only from the spiritual perspective, but also from the therapeutic point of view.

That is why TFT has an important task to achieve in the spiritual realm. If you compare the main list of mental disorders treated by TFT and the above mentioned sicknesses of the soul, you will find a perfect correlation.

It has been my experience in the spiritual field that TFT opens a door to God's grace and makes possible spiritual healing for people who have been suffering.

—*Father Luis Jorge González, PhD*

Tapping to Help Conquer Addictions

You'll find videos that step you through the complete tapping sequence for curbing addictive urges at our website:

www.rogercallahan.com/pathways

12

Chapter Twelve: Using Thought Field Therapy to Create Better Outcomes

As we developed Thought Field Therapy over the years and refined the specific tapping sequences for different disorders, it eventually became apparent that tapping was working almost in spite of a patient's hesitancy. It was almost as TFT was overriding the mind's own aversion to change and that neither the therapist nor the patient needed to believe that TFT worked—or even care whether it worked.

It simply did.

This led us to explore other ways of using TFT, not just to relieve specific disorders, but also to bring about lifestyle improvement, better athletic ability, business success and other types of positive outcomes.

We began to believe that any goal was possible with TFT.

Perhaps you are like more and more people today for whom the world seems to be spinning out of control. Goals that seemed so much closer during the "boom years" now appear further away than ever.

Many people are questioning how they can get what they want when—every day—they're feeling more and more lost, helpless and stressed. Daily news stories keep us focused on negative, stressful events—rather than on pursuing our goals, dreams and desires.

If you've found yourself falling further into this "mental mind-trap," TFT can help you stay focused, optimistic, calm and resourceful. It can help you maintain an action-oriented posture versus numbly reacting to whatever comes your way. And in this state of calm and focus, your own personal super-computer—the brain—can do its job of scanning your environment, looking for connections, allowing opportunity to filter into your consciousness... and giving you the motivation and desire to act.

What positive outcomes can TFT bring into *your* life?

If you've been recently unemployed and want to find new

work, TFT can help activate your job-seeking abilities by allowing your stress-free mind to act upon chance encounters, forgotten connections and odd conversations.

If financial success is your goal, TFT can help you find *and act upon* opportunities to make more money than you ever dreamed possible. Significant riches ARE being made in this financial climate by people who can identify them and move forward with confidence.

If you want to meet your soulmate, TFT can help you finally release the emotional hurts and deep-seated "baggage" of past relationships—allowing you to be open to new love and happiness again.

If superb health and relief from annoying or cumbersome disease and disorders is your goal, TFT can immediately reduce the stress that causes these ailments—and reduce the further stress they cause *you* in living with them. The American Institute of Stress found that over 90% of disease is caused or complicated by stress. In fact, stress is a leading contributor to *all chronic diseases* such as heart disease, stroke, cancer, chronic respiratory disease and diabetes.

Thought Field Therapy can also help you take control and conquer your fears, jealousy, depression, obsessions and compulsions, anger, grief, addictive urges, self-sabotage, and irrational guilt—putting you on the path to peak performance, effective weight control, improved self-esteem, and so much more.

Because the tapping sequences work directly on the energy meridians of the body and simultaneously relieve harmful emotions that are stored in these pathways, TFT can free you to allow abundance, confidence and tranquility back into your life.

We've included some of our very favorite stories in this final chapter to give you a glimpse of the success you, too, could enjoy once you apply TFT to eliminating your stressful conditions and to opening your mind and emotions to improving every area of your life.

Get Ready for the "Consequences" of TFT

Shortly before attending a TFT diagnostic training several years ago, I decided to try an experiment and tap on myself whenever anything negative was going on in my head. Over a short period of time, this developed into a habit and I was tapping several times a day. I tapped at stoplights, in my office, in the bathroom—whenever I thought about it. It just feels kind of good! This has evolved into tapping just three or four times a day, even though I am not thinking about anything in particular.

Several months later, I noticed that I had not been sick. No colds, no flu, no sickness of any kind—not even my yearly winter sinus infection that required two months of antibiotics to cure. I noticed that I was tapping three or four times whenever I got a scratchy throat or a hint of achy joints or anything that felt a little "off." Whatever the minor affliction, the problem would disappear in a couple of hours. Most often, I wouldn't even notice that it was gone. It has been 2½ years now and still no ailments of any kind. None!

Now, I can't prove that tapping is doing this, but I have never had this level of physical health before and there is nothing else that I am doing differently.

—Don Walker

* * *

Thought Field Therapy doesn't just work on keeping you healthy, it can also help you expand possibilities for your life as you overcome roadblocks that previously held you back.

In one of our favorite stories, a man who lives a lifetime unable to read or write, finally overcomes a childhood learning disability and pursues a brand new career. Willingly, like many people who learn TFT, once he sees the benefit of TFT in his own life, he dedicates himself to discovering other ways to use TFT—for himself, for his family and for others around him.

All My Life, I Lived With This Secret

This letter is long overdue, but I had a good reason why I couldn't send it earlier. Roger and Joanne from the bottom of my heart, I thank you so much for this amazing therapy that's helped me in so many areas in my life by removing all of my personal blocks and barriers.

Just three years ago at the age of 48, I was unable to use a computer and spell a half-decent paragraph. All of my life I had this secret and never shared it with anyone. I had a childhood learning disability that led to near-illiteracy in adulthood.

While I was very successful in the food industry for more than 25 years, every time I made a career move, I would delegate all of my paper work and anything to do with computers to my staff and bookkeepers.

Then at age 37, I started to read my first book. One day in the library, a book—your book—fell onto the floor, and I picked it up and read it.

It took me two months to finish it, but I soon signed up for a training TFT course to help me remove all the fears and phobias I had from school in the early 1970s. The learning disability I had throughout my life was very hard to cope with in school and with my friends.

For the first few years after taking the TFT training, I did treatments on myself and I was truly happy with the outcome. Even though I had problems learning in school, I knew I had a higher calling. I just didn't know what it was at the time. For me, the First Miracle came when Thought Field Therapy removed the urge for drinking alcohol.

I had gotten married at age 43—and nine months after the day I stopped drinking alcohol, my daughter Marina was born. For years, I had wanted a little girl to call my own. This was the Second Miracle that I received from TFT.

The Third Miracle happened when Marina was three years old.

Week after week, she would scream at the top of her lungs in the middle of the night. She had nightmares, and they were getting worse and lasting longer as the weeks went by. Marina kept telling us, "Spiders are all over the floor." We were at our wit's end, until one night I said to my wife, "I have all this great material on how to remove fears and phobias, and I don't even use it on others."

So I decided to read most of the TFT material the next day, and two nights later, my daughter started to scream again at 3:00 in the morning.

My wife and I took Marina in to our room, and I started to treat her with Thought Field Therapy—hoping it would release the majority of the phobia. Within five minutes, she calmed down and we took her back to her own bedroom. Two minutes later, she ran back to us and said, "Daddy, Daddy, the dots worked! I don't see the spiders anymore."

Because I had been tapping on her pressure points with my fingers, Marina had called tapping by another name...dots.

I looked at my wife and said, "I need to follow this sign and take Thought Field Therapy training one more time."

On the last day of the training, I told Joanne, "All of my life, I've had problems comprehending information in school. I've taken High School English five to six times in my life, and my highest mark was 23% on average." Joanne then did a TFT treatment with me to release a personal block I had for more than 40 years regarding spelling and writing.

In the 18 months since that treatment (as you can see from this letter), I've been writing, spelling and using the computer like there's no tomorrow! I've also become a certified life coach and am now helping people with all of *their* personal blocks and barriers. This is the first time in my life that I truly feel inspired, fulfilled and living my calling.

I'm also in the beginning stages of writing my first book. All of the problems I had in school just vanished after a few treatments of Thought Field Therapy.

—*Franco Manna*

* * *

If Thought Field Therapy can help overcome the challenge of learning to read and write, could it also help a highly educated person find employment after months of desperately looking for work? In this next story—which is also a testament to the positive effects of TFT done in a group setting—we discover how tapping created a positive future for one man—and a positive discovery for the people who tapped along with him.

The "Guinea Pig" Gets a Phone Call

Jim had been in ill health and out of work for three months when he went to the Tapping Support Group on August 4th. That morning, Jim had undergone a procedure where he was anesthetized and a shock treatment was administered to get his heart back into rhythm. He was tired, uncomfortable, and still somewhat drugged from the morning experience. Nevertheless, he decided to go to the meeting to reap the benefits of the energy created when a group of like-minded people tap together.

At the meeting, the primary focus was Jim—whom we affectionately called "The Guinea Pig." We were trying to help him because we realized how serious his situation had become. Not only was he suffering from a lack of work, but—at 60 years of age—there were few job prospects for him. In addition, he had two children in college, significant health challenges, and a huge mortgage to pay.

As Jim later told us, "The bottom line is that I believe all these good things would not have happened if I had not been to the TFT tapping session. Dariah and Bruce were both willing to work with me on the issues I was facing. They helped me with the TFT process to resolve my issues and move forward in life." As we tapped, we focused on specific thoughts we believed would help:

- That Jim would move forward from a perception of lack to a knowing that all is possible
- That there was a right job for him using his skills in a way that benefits the environment and mankind
- That there would be enough salary to support his family, and
- That he would not have to relocate.

Following the tapping support group meeting, Jim had what he called "a spiritual message" that he should check the Denbury website (an oil and gas company near Jim's home) for possible positions that he would be qualified for. He had applied for a senior project position with them months earlier—only to receive a "Dear John" letter saying that, though he was highly qualified and they appreciated his inquiry, the application process was closed.

Six days after our group tapping session, Jim got another spiritual message that he should contact Denbury again expressing his interest in the company—which he did. He mentioned that he wanted stay in the Dallas area as both of his grown children lived there.

As Jim told us later, "I also told them that I believe very strongly in Denbury's vision as a corporation and also felt they had an excellent long-term business plan. I have been highly interested in using my skills as a Chemical Engineer in the oil and gas industry in environmentally positive ways for many years. I had pinpointed Denbury as the number one company in the area where I could realize my dream of contributing to the long-term health of our planet in this manner."

Jim sent them a follow-up email and received a phone call the very next day requesting an immediate phone interview!

"The two-hour phone interview went so well," Jim said, "they requested a face-to-face meeting. That four-hour meeting went extremely well and, at the end of the day, they said they would contact me on Monday to let me know if I'd be receiving a job offer."

On Monday, the call came through. Denbury would be presenting a formal job offer within the next two days. As it happened, the offer was "far beyond anything that I could have imagined, and very generous," Jim said. He accepted the offer with the request that he begin work the following Monday.

Just two weeks to the day after our group tapping session—when Jim had had no job possibilities on the horizon—he was at work again.

—Dr. Dariah Morgan, PhD and Dr. Bruce R. Paton

* * *

More and more, people from all walks of life are using Thought Field Therapy to overcome challenges and create better outcomes for themselves. In this next story, a teacher recognizes that her students—growing up in an area of widespread poverty, illiteracy and drug addiction—need special help.

TFT in the Classroom

After taking a TFT personal development class, I wondered if I might be able to use what I had learned with my Kindergarten class. The children I work with live on the Leeward side of the island of Oahu, where a large portion of our Native Hawaiian population resides and there is high rate of poverty, illiteracy and drug addiction. Many of my students come from young single-parent families and have been exposed to drugs, as well as both physical and emotional abuse.

Despite all of these obstacles, most of these children still have the desire to learn, and—with the help of TFT—I've been able to increase their ability to focus and concentrate on their class work.

Each day after recess, I lead my class through the collarbone breathing exercise to help them "cool off" and focus on their next subject. One day I forgot to "cool off" and began our next lesson studying the names of colors. The children began yelling out the color names, "Blue! Red! Green!" in such a frenetic manner that it made me realize we had not done our collarbone breathing exercise. I quickly led the class through the exercise and immediately there was tranquility in the room, after which the children quietly named the colors as they were shown.

After consulting with Joanne Callahan, I have also begun using TFT to help children with letter reversals*. I either show the child how to tap on their hand or tap it for them myself.

---

* Many children reverse letters when first learning to write, substituting "p" for "q" and "b" for "d," for example. While just a normal developmental stage in younger children, it can be a problem as children get older if not corrected.

After the tapping, the children are able to write correctly with no reversals. This worked particularly well with a special education student who copied everything with reversed lettering. After noticing this pattern, I had her tap on the side of her hand to correct the psychological reversal and when she redid her work, she copied it perfectly!

Our system of using TFT works so well that the children are now reminding me to do it regularly. The beauty of TFT is that it is so simple to use, and yet it is so effective. An investment of a few minutes each day reaps limitless bounty for learning. Thank you for this incredible tool.

—Cathy Tanida

* * *

Children respond extremely well to TFT. Of course, a child does not need to know how it works or even agree with the procedure in order to get a benefit. But they do understand how good they feel while doing TFT.

In this next story—about a special group of students—one TFT practitioner uses tapping to alleviate the stress of bullying at school, putting students in a stronger, more confident state.

"I'll Do Anything to Make It Stop"

"You are fat, stupid and ugly." This is just one example of the taunting that some students endure from peers and classmates. These and other harmful statements are instances of bullying.

Bullying is a form of violence. It is negative, aggressive and unwanted behaviors intended to cause harm, hurt or humiliation to another student. It is anything that hurts another student, when things are repeatedly said or done to have power over that individual.

There are many types of bullying, including racial bullying, sexual bullying and cyber bullying. Bullying includes name calling, saying or writing derogatory comments, purposely excluding an individual from activities, spreading lies and rumors, ignoring, threatening, doing anything to make another person feel uncomfortable or scared, stealing or damaging belongings of others, kicking, hitting, slapping, and making someone do things they do not want to do.

Children handle being bullied in many different ways. Those who are bullied are subject to peer pressure. Sometimes they end up doing things they really do not want to do in order to "fit in"—hoping that the bullying will stop. Those who are bullied often feel pain, fear or hurt. They lose self-confidence and feel lonely, scared and sad. They sometimes do not feel safe at school, at home or at play—and often have poor grades in school. They may suffer from depression, headaches, stomach aches and other health problems and they may also have thoughts of suicide. Some feel it necessary to fight or bring a gun or weapon to school to stop the hurt of being bullied.

I worked with a group of middle-school students who felt they were being bullied. The students were referred to me by their parents because they where getting into trouble at school. Many of the students were receiving declining or failing grades. Some of them had experienced detentions or suspensions for fighting inside or outside of school.

When meeting with the students for the first time, they explained the reason they got into fights was because they felt they were being "picked on." A group of students constantly bullied them, and they got into the fights because they felt angry and wanted to lash out against the bullying.

Statistics reveal that one out of every four students are bullied, picked on, or abused each month. In addition, 30% of students in the United States admit to being bullies, victims of bullies, bystanders of bullying or have participated in all three roles.

My work with the group began with explaining Thought Field Therapy to try to solve the anxiety, fear and feeling that they had to fight to end the bullying. The students rated their SUD (*subjective units of distress*) which ranged from "10" or above for fear and anxiety to "7." I began leading the students through Psychological Reversal to correct any reversals that may negatively effect the treatment. I then taught them the tapping sequence for General Anxiety and Stress, checking frequently for SUD as their distress steadily lowered by at least two points for all students in the group.

We continued in this way until the SUD for each student was down to "0" or "1." The students reported feeling better and explained that "feeling better" meant they where having fun doing TFT and did not feel tense or angry when they thought about being bullied.

Studies show that the less confidence a student has, the more likely they are to be bullied. The more confidence a student presents, the less likely it is that bullying will occur. They continued to practice the steps of TFT until they learned the sequences well enough to do them throughout the week whenever they felt like fighting, felt scared or felt less confident.

When the students arrived the next week, they were laughing and talking with a completely different demeanor from the previous week when they where somber, sad and angry. The students reported having used TFT throughout the week. All of them explained that they did not participate in any fights during the week. They all told of using tapping when feeling scared.

One student explained that she was able to concentrate on her school work and was able to pass her math test because—for the first time—she was able to study. But the most compelling comment came from one student who was constantly engaged in fighting and was on the verge of being expelled from school, even though she was actually the victim of bullying.

"I didn't fight when some kids were picking on me," she said. "I just started tapping and walked away."

—Dr. Victoria Yancey

* * *

Who else can use Thought Field Therapy to create better outcomes? Well, athletes use tapping all the time. Professional athletes have long known about alternative therapies that help them focus on their goals, accomplish important plays and master "the head game" of their chosen sport.

In this next story about world-class athletes who use TFT, we get a glimpse of how anyone can use tapping to overcome challenges, erase setbacks and eliminate roadblocks to getting what they want.

 A Revolution in Sports

As a speaker in the sports world, I often give presentations to professional athletes, their coaches and trainers. Recently, I presented the topic "Be the Best You Can Be" for one of Norway's top female teams in European team handball.

I described how they could eliminate nervousness when competing against the best players in the world. I also told how to recover mentally from injuries, how to create an unbeatable belief in yourself, how to find the way to your "zone" whenever you want, and how to "create flow" with TFT.

I was asked to give the speech to this team in particular because I had treated their female trainer with TFT four years earlier when she was still a player—waiting for an operation to repair a shoulder injury. After an MRI scan, the doctors told her that one ligament was torn completely and two were torn partially. It took just four minutes via telephone to reduce her shoulder pain from an SUD (*subjective units of distress*) of "7" to "1."

Over the next three days, she played eight matches in the annual Veterans Championship, becoming their top scorer with six goals in the final match—all thrown with the arm that had "torn" ligaments. After her win, she trained with weights nearly every day and went on to play at the top level in Norway for the last four years—a major accomplishment since Norway is the reigning world champion in the sport and competition in the top ranks is fierce.

In another interesting example of the profound power of using TFT for sports, Norway's top go-cart driver sent me a text message, saying "TFT rules!"

He had just won a big competition in Germany, and over the two previous weekends had finished 2nd in both Monaco and Italy. He is just 14 years old, and his results have never before been matched by anyone in Norway. And these achievements were after I had worked with him for just six months.

And finally, Norway's first professional men's soccer team to use TFT advanced to play in the Norwegian Cup Final. They reported seeing much better results than expected. My colleague Mette Rosseland and I have worked with them over the last six months.

One of their best players continually had problems getting back into the game whenever he made a mistake. I traced this limiting performance to a trauma at age 15 when he had a skin condition and took medication that created social anxiety.

We immediately treated the trauma, which eliminated his problems in the game. As it turns out, he had been afraid of the media attention that would follow—whether he played poorly or admirably—because the cameras would expose his former skin condition. He has since been their most reliable player, even if he is only 20 years old.

The women's soccer team had equally beneficial results with TFT. Though they were not favored to win going into the Norwegian Cup Final, they used TFT in the locker room after having seen the results with their male counterparts. While they had been playing badly going into the finals, they ended up winning with a score of 7-0. Not bad!

Before I learned Thought Field Therapy, I was an acknowledged mental trainer in sports. Now I can truly state that TFT has meant a total revolution in the area of mental sports performance.

—*Mats J. Uldal*

* * *

TFT is no stranger to the sports world. In this next story, one of Saudi Arabia's most popular soccer teams discovers the benefits of "mental conditioning" using tapping to relieve stress before the game. But this story has a twist—a team makes the finals bringing with them a 15-year losing streak they must overcome.

 ## "The Burden on Us Is Heavy"

The Kingdom of Saudi Arabia is well known for its soccer teams. For 16 consecutive years, the national soccer team of Saudi Arabia has won against every national team of the Asian countries. One of our most famous teams—a team in the premiere league of Saudi Arabia—used to win a lot of the Cup Finals in our country. Yet, recently, even with their incredible history, millions of fans and numerous wealthy princes supporting them, they had failed to win a title in more than 15 years.

Before I began working with them, they would easily reach the finals—only to lose when playing against their major rivals—another team from the same premiere league. No matter what they did, they would end up meeting this team, either in the finals or the semi-finals.

And they would lose.

I guess you could say the players had developed a phobia for this other team. Match after match, they would lose to their rivals.

Not only did the teams meet in the final match of the Prince Faysal Bin Fahad Cup—but to make matters worse, they were to meet again two weeks later in the finals of the Crown Prince Cup.

With so many previous losses looming on the horizon, even their most loyal fans were beginning to say that the team simply could not win. I was asked to do some psychological preparation for the players. Of course, they had the best possible training, superb technical advice, the right salaries (with financial promises if they won), even the best coach.

Yet tension was still high.

During my first session with them, when I asked the players how they felt about the upcoming match, I got no answers. Just silence and a few muffled murmurs. I knew the players were thinking about every mistake they'd ever made on the field and every match they'd ever lost. They couldn't get past their losses to think about the wins that had helped them make it to the finals.

Then I explained that an American scientist, Dr. Roger Callahan, had discovered there are tapping points on our body—that, if we tap them in a certain sequence, release the stress in our minds. I could see a few of the players sitting up a little straighter.

Again I asked, "How do you feel now when you think of your upcoming match?"

This time, one of their stars said he felt stressed. "We want to win," he said. "We're given all that we need to win, and everyone is asking us to win. But they're also saying, 'Don't fail us.' That makes the burden on us even heavier."

"What happens when a player is stressed?" I asked.

They all knew the answer. One said he felt weak in his heels. Another felt as though he couldn't control the ball. Still another knew that, under stress, a player could easily make a wrong move, play too harshly on the field, and maybe get a red card that would put him out of the game.

One player who came forward—one of the stars of the team, said that on a scale of 1 to 10, his stress felt like a "10."

I quickly tapped under his eye, under his arm and under his collarbone—explaining that these points were linked to stress in our bodies and minds. I repeated the sequence two more times and the player said his distress had dropped to a "3," then a "1" and then "0." You could see the change in his face. He relaxed. Something was going on inside him.

When I asked him again how he felt, he said his tension was gone. Better yet, he could see himself playing great, cool, with his heels limber, yet steady on the ground. "The ball is obeying me," he said. His face was beaming with happiness.

When I asked for another volunteer, a young player came forward. He was bent low and visibly stressed. His hands felt like ice. He looked at me with a pale nervous smile. He felt as though his feet were tied with ropes, so great was his distress. A "10" on the SUD scale, without a doubt.

I used the same tapping sequence on him, but his SUD remained high, so I took his hand and began to tap on the side to correct for psychological reversal. Steadily, his distress dropped to a "5," then a "3," then to "0."

Asking all the players at once to think about their stress, I talked them through the tapping sequence until their SUD had dropped to "0." Whenever they felt worried or anxious, I said, tap these points.

"You might feel tense on the bus on your way to the stadium," I said. "Or if you think of the final match at night in your room and find it difficult to sleep, tap again."

In the final match that week, the team won out against their rival with a score of 3-0. A few weeks later, they played the rival team again—and still they won...with a score of 2-1.

The phobia was broken, the past was undone. TFT helped them do that.

—*Abdulhamid Mustafa AlFirdaus*

* * *

What other kinds of sports can Thought Field Therapy help with? Well, for decades, TFT has been helping golfers improve their game—whether they're international pros or local amateur players.

Thought Field Therapy helps golfers master their "head game"—allowing them to not only improve their technique, but also execute important shots with consistency. For players who do great on the driving range only to land it in the rough or lose their short game by the back nine, TFT helps them relax, concentrate, and transmit all their expensive training into finding their authentic swing. Suddenly, they place ball after ball exactly where they want them. Slicing and mis-hits become a thing of the past. They can finally plan and execute their most difficult putts.

In this next story of three different golfers, TFT helps them not only play a better round of golf—they find they enjoy the game much more, too.

Three Days in the Sixties

The application of TFT to promoting life and health is unlimited. In yet another example, it can help increase one's enjoyment and performance of various sports.

For example, Dr. Robert Blaich, a chiropractor, worked with world-class athletes and found that simply correcting for psychological reversal· could make the difference between success and failure, in winning and losing.

It is often said that the main difference between top athletes is a psychological difference. My experience with top athletes supports this notion.

Three professional golfers I treated boosted their performance to even better heights than they were able to achieve prior to treatment. And over the years, I have heard of a number of golf instructors who use Thought Field Therapy in teaching golfers how to remove blocks from their game.

The Yips

The first pro golfer I treated was a spectacular athlete and was a hall-of-fame winner in another sport. However, he suffered from what golfers call "the yips." That is, his game broke down after he got on the green. His putts were terrible. Being a keen competitor, this bothered him very much, and when he heard that I might be able to help, he immediately came to me for treatment.

I only needed to see him once. Yet his game immediately improved dramatically. He even laughed about the charge for treatment and said that he more than made it back his first day just on side bets!

The last I heard from him he was being interviewed on television for winning a tournament that up until that time, had eluded him.

∗ Psychological reversal (or "PR") is a blockage or reversal of the energy flows in your body's energy pathways. It keeps all kinds of treatments from working as well as they should. PR can be easily eliminated by tapping midway on the outside edge of your hand prior to using other tapping sequences for your illness or disorder. TFT practitioners always test for PR prior to TFT treatment.

Young Talent

My next golfer client was a young man just beginning to turn pro. He was referred to me by a very talented European psychiatrist who had worked with him over a period of years, and helped him with many problems. His teachers and colleagues predicted great things for him, but something was still holding him back.

I treated him while he was in Europe with the advanced TFT procedure, Voice Technology, and rapidly cleared up a number of personal concerns. Also, I examined him for various aspects of his game and treated him. The next day, he was in a tournament and fell apart on the very aspects for which I had successfully treated him. I knew in principle that the problem had to be one of toxins.

It was necessary to find out what was hurting his game after he had been so successfully treated. I found that one of his habits was to order a pizza every night before playing. Although this might have been OK for some people—for him, Voice Technology revealed that pizza was a toxin. He was thrilled to discover this and laid off the pizza. I treated him again which took only minutes.

A week later, I watched on an international golf channel as he played the final day in a major tournament. The television commentator remarked on the fact that since the beginning of play, my client's score for each of the three days was in the sixties! He did great in his first try against top international competition and came in second.

Incidentally, it is not only that a toxin can undo a treatment, but our bodies hold water after we ingest a toxin, and this alone can throw off our timing, effect our judgment, and create anxiety. Toxins are not good for anyone; but for elite athletes they can cause terrible transformations—commonly called "the slumps."

Top Amateur

One of my favorite golf stories is that of a man in his late seventies who loved golf and played every day. When he couldn't get any friends to play, he would play with a young pro. The man, a physician, was also terribly bothered by severe gastrointestinal problems for years, which he could not understand.

When he heard that I might be able to help his golf game, he called me immediately. I treated him for all aspects of his game, then he mentioned something that told me volumes about his difficulty. He said that his game on the first nine holes was very good, but that it fell apart on the back nine. One might assume that naturally this elderly man would get tired after nine holes. However, the tiredness did not progress hole by hole but took a quantum down turn right after the first nine. Curious, I started asking questions. What happened after the first nine?

As it turns out, he typically took a break and ate a lunch he brought with him. I checked everything and found that wheat was a toxin for this man. I told him to stop eating wheat, and instead, go to a health-food store and buy spelt-grain bread as a substitute. He followed my directions carefully and the next time out on the golf course, he beat the pro!

His gastrointestinal problems simply disappeared, too, suggesting that wheat was also behind this problem.

—*Roger J. Callahan, PhD*

Tapping for Better Outcomes

You'll find videos that step you through the complete tapping sequence for creating positive outcomes at our website:

www.rogercallahan.com/pathways

Conclusion

After 30 years of reading stories and client case studies like the ones featured in this book, we're convinced—more than ever—that TFT is doing something within the body that is fundamentally different from anything offered by the medical profession or alternative healthcare practitioners.

By accessing the body's own energy pathways, Thought Field Therapy is activating and stimulating the body's own healing systems—allowing rapid relief to occur and complete healing to begin. By reducing stress, erasing harmful stored emotions, clearing energy blockages and "re-organizing" the way the brain and body reacts to anxiety, stress, illness, trauma and other situations, TFT has the power to abolish illness and disease as an inevitable by-product of mental and emotional turmoil.

But make no mistake. TFT doesn't just mask symptoms or cover up real dangers that should be addressed medically. It is much wiser than that as this brief practitioner letter will show.

 ## The Wisdom of Thought Field Therapy

Every now and then, there's a discussion amongst TFT practitioners about the wisdom of treating nausea with TFT. The discussion usually centers on the belief that nausea may be the body's natural, intelligent response to the ingestion of a toxic substance and may therefore promote health by encouraging the individual to stay away from the particular food or drink that's creating the discomfort.

This natural protection system could be even more vital in the case of pregnant women, as the nausea may be a means of protecting the developing fetus from exposure to a toxic substance repeatedly ingested by the mother.

Several years ago, soon after my advanced training in TFT diagnostics, I treated an 87-year-old woman for nausea, the outcome of which surprised and fascinated me. This client, whom I'll call "Bea," was temporarily in a nursing home as a result of having fallen and broken her pelvis two weeks earlier. While in this facility, she developed a constant case of nausea so strong that she could hardly "stomach" the mere mention of food, much less eat it. This quickly became a life-threatening situation for Bea since she only weighed 108 pounds and was rapidly losing weight, as well as the will to live.

I visited Bea in the nursing home to see if TFT might help relieve her nausea. After first determining a custom TFT sequence through diagnostics, I tapped on her myself since she was too weak and unfocused to do so herself. Within two or three minutes of the treatment, Bea vomited.

My immediate reaction to this was dismay and concern.

I soon realized, however, how wisely and beautifully the tool of TFT performed. First of all, I learned that Bea had not been able to vomit since she was 12 years old, and because of this had endured many bouts of extreme indigestion and nausea throughout her lifetime, without any relief from vomiting. Secondly, by vomiting her body was able to rid itself of possible offending substances, which a mere fading of the nausea would not have achieved.

Bea's nausea actually returned the next day, which prompted an examination by a gastroenterologist who found the basic problem—a bleeding ulcer. It is important to note that, even though TFT was able to give her temporary relief, enable her body to rid itself of a possibly irritating substance, and remove a lifelong block to vomiting, it did not permanently remove or cover up the symptom (i.e., nausea) that was part of a deeper problem.

—Mary L. Cowley, PhD

* * *

As we've mentioned before in this book, TFT heals, relieves, eliminates and calms, yet throughout that process of healing, it has been self-applied for over 30 years with no reported cases of harm. It doesn't mask symptoms that might be an indicator of a greater problem—but even more importantly, it produces no side effects of its own, as most pharmaceutical drugs, surgeries and other traditional medical treatments do. It further heals trauma and emotional disorders without requiring patients to "relive" and suffer a second time through the traumatic episode in the therapist's office—as so many recognized "therapies" do.

For this reason it can—and we believe *should*—work within the traditional medical and therapeutic fields as a secondary "treatment" to aid recovery from illness and remove the underlying psychological causes of disease.

Today, hundreds of traditional medical practitioners are starting to recognize the value of Thought Field Therapy in the healing process. It is fast, effective and low cost. And it fits within the confines of many busy medical practices which are, more and more, limited in the amount of time and attention they can extend to each individual patient.

In this next story from a midwife in Australia, TFT corrects a troubling problem—and astounds doctors by its results.

 ## TFT Works Within the Traditional Medical Field

At the time I attended the TFT training in Sydney, I was about 21 weeks pregnant. I had just finished my midwifery training and was excited to incorporate TFT into my practice as a homebirth midwife. In fact, the midwife for my own pregnancy, Lianne Schwartz, also attended the training following many discussions and experiences of the benefits of TFT.

Prior to the training, however, we were both concerned about the separation of my abdominal muscle as the baby grew. My uterus was also quite firm to the touch and it seemed that the uterine muscles would spasm unpredictably.

During the TFT course, I treated my abdominal muscles for psychological reversal. Then, while learning advanced TFT procedures, I focused on this same issue. Immediately after the advanced treatment, I noticed that my belly appeared to be a different shape. When I had Lianne examine my abdomen, we were amazed to find that the muscle separation had diminished from its original four fingers in width to about 1-2 fingers in width from my navel upwards. Below my navel, the muscles had completely come together.

This kind of change is unheard of.

In fact, other women have required surgery after birth for muscle separation that was similar to the extent of mine. My uterus was also soft and did not spasm as it had done in the past.

Since the training, I have treated my uterus and abdominal muscles when needed for psychological reversal and they have remained healthy and strong—with the muscle separation still only about one centimeter, which is great for this stage of pregnancy. I have also used TFT on myself throughout the pregnancy with great success to test for and treat environmental and ingested toxins, necessary supplements, nausea, vomiting and various emotional issues.

Since the TFT training, both Lianne and I have had incredible experiences and outcomes using TFT with women and families in the prenatal period, during the births we have attended, and in the postnatal period.

One of our cases involved the same problem that I had experienced with my abdominal muscles. A client who had her first baby five years ago and her second baby two years ago, was still having problems with a large separation. After two pregnancies, a 3.5-finger width separation remained. She had been seeing both a physiotherapist who specialized in postnatal issues for women and an osteopath for the past two years.

This woman decided to try TFT, and after one treatment session with Lianne, her abdominal muscles rebound to only a one centimeter separation. A week later, she visited her osteopath without telling him about her TFT treatment, as she wanted an objective opinion. He was astounded at the change and even consulted his notes to confirm his original diagnosis and that there had been no change in the past two years—until now.

He was very excited when she told him about TFT.

Another area we have been treating women for is previous traumatic birth experiences. We see more and more women with disempowering and difficult birth experiences within the hospital system. Statistics in Australia show that one in three women experience postnatal depression—with a similarly high number of women suffering from Post-Traumatic Stress Disorder following their birth experience.

—*Pia Cowley*

* * *

Whether you are a medical practitioner or just wanting to take control of your own physical and mental well-being, TFT can provide an extraordinary new lifestyle of health, harmony and vitality. If you've been wondering how you can further your knowledge of Thought Field therapy and learn to use with your own symptoms and life situations, you can always read more about our training programs and in-depth learning products for specific disorders at www.rogercallahan.com/pathways.

But before you visit our website, read this final story about a woman who gave herself the gift of TFT knowledge.

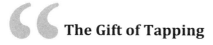

The Gift of Tapping

This year for my birthday, I chose to attend the TFT Boot Camp in California. Not many people would celebrate their special day at a weekend seminar. In fact, I could hear the surprise in the voices of my family and friends when I declined their invitations to get together because I was attending this boot camp instead. Little did I know that this gift I chose to give myself would turn out to be a gift that keeps on "giving back."

Unlike most of the other attendees, I didn't have any previous experience with tapping nor did I hold any degrees or certifications in the healing arts. All I had under my belt was a strong belief that I had found a powerful tool coupled with a strong desire to learn. Minute by minute my confidence grew as Joanne Callahan, Dr. Roger Callahan and Dr. Robert "Bob" Bray expertly led us through a very intense hands-on workshop. I saw before my eyes fellow trainees, myself included, overcome phobias, traumas, blocks, addictions and other issues. Although I was exhausted while driving home that Sunday evening, I couldn't ignore the excitement that was surging through me. I knew right away that my life would never be the same.

The very next morning, I made up my mind that I would make full use of this newly gained knowledge. So I immediately set about recruiting and working with clients in order to complete my TFT diagnostic certification.

One of the reasons for my haste was that I'd be boarding a plane for the Dominican Republic just four days after I attended the boot camp. I knew if I didn't continue moving forward while excitement and momentum were still on my side, just one week of vacation could easily start the ball of procrastination rolling.

My first chance to put TFT to work came sooner than I expected on my second day in the Dominican Republic. While speaking with a fellow sitting next to me at the convention we were both attending, he mentioned that he had been suffering from neck and shoulder pain. I eagerly offered my service— knowing that I could assist him in gaining some relief. He eagerly accepted and didn't waste much time suggesting we should do the diagnosis and treatment during the lunch break.

How glad I was that I chose to pack my Boot Camp Manual and notes instead of my favorite hair dryer! The session lasted no longer than fifteen minutes, but we were able to discuss the merits of the technique for far longer! He was so thrilled that his neck pain went from a SUD of "8" down to "0" that he planned to encourage his massage therapist daughter to attend the boot camp, as well. I checked with him several times that day, as well as the next day, and his neck continued to remain pain-free. Word of his pain relief soon spread and before the afternoon was over, I had already promised to treat two ladies and gave "rain checks" to a few others since the tight convention schedule prevented me from helping more people.

Both ladies were grateful for the treatment results and both showed interest in learning more. It felt wonderful to be able to help these individuals and spread the good word about this amazing technique!

I can honestly say that I haven't gone a day without either tapping on myself or assisting someone else with tapping. I have used it on physical issues like hiccups, sore throats, headaches, stuffy noses and back pain. I have helped myself as well as others get over emotional issues and even phobias. Even my dog has had the pleasure of being tapped! I have been kept busy with the many friends and family that are eagerly waiting to learn and use this treatment in their own lives.

I am constantly relying on the immediate relief tapping brings me from daily stress and unexpected anxieties. There seems to be no issue that cannot reap some benefit or relief from this technique. So I am constantly on the lookout for more opportunities to share this wonderful tool with anyone who is willing to listen. Whether it be on a zip line platform where nerves get a little frazzled or in an endless line of frustrated customers at the post office or while teaching children in a Brazilian jiu-jitsu class, I stand ready knowing that this invaluable tool will bring relief from any issue that might arise.

Perhaps the most amazing opportunity came when I learned that my parents decided to attend a family birthday dinner that I was also invited to. Certain events in the recent past have occurred that have caused a substantial rift between us. It was very tempting to cancel my plans and avoid them further, but having this effective tool to heal myself from the trauma they caused gave me no excuse to attend right along with them.

The anger and anxiety from a still-unresolved situation they had put me in seemed to melt away as I tapped myself in preparation of our first meeting. I greeted my father with a cheerful "Happy Birthday!" followed by a hug. I expected some negative feelings to creep back in, but none did. Then I similarly greeted my mother. They were both pleasantly surprised at my sincere and warm reception. They had no idea that, just an hour before, I had contemplated not seeing them at all and even dwelled on feelings of hurt, frustration, betrayal and anger. I amazed many of my family members that night by my complete lack of negativity towards my parents, as they all know the extent of our issues.

As my last gift to my father, before I went home that night, I offered to diagnose and treat his foot that had been swollen with gout for almost two years. The initial treatment didn't produce complete relief, but I encouraged him to continue tapping on his own. The next day, my mother reported that the swelling had disappeared and so had the pain! I truly believe that his foot was not the only thing that was healed that night—for, with that small gesture I offered him, a way had been paved to heal our relationship, as well.

As I end this letter, I would like to share the exciting news that a professional athlete has agreed to meet with me so I can explain the benefits he could gain towards peak performance through tapping. He is quite intrigued, and I sincerely hope I can assist in furthering his promising career. It continues to amaze me how wide and varied are the range of situations where I can apply TFT techniques.

I have complete faith that—with more experience and my continued willingness to seek more training and knowledge—I will be able to change many more lives. I am extremely grateful that I have had the privilege to learn this technique and in turn share this amazing gift with others.

—Ann Marjorie Alayon

About the Authors

Dr. Roger Callahan

Founder and developer of the Callahan Techniques® Thought Field Therapy, Roger J. Callahan, Ph.D., is a clinical psychologist. A graduate of the University of Michigan, he received his Ph.D. in clinical psychology from Syracuse University.

He is the recipient of a Lifetime Achievement award from the Association for Comprehensive Energy Psychology for his 30-year career in developing and enhancing Thought Field Therapy as an accepted treatment used widely by therapists and other professionals.

Dr. Callahan is the author of numerous works published in nearly a dozen languages on the subject of psychological health and recovery including: *It Can Happen to You: The Practical Guide to Romantic Love* (a Book-of-the-Month Club selection); *The Callahan Anxiety Pictures* (a projective test to measure anxiety); *The Five Minute Phobia Cure*; and *The Anxiety Addiction Connection.* Additionally, he is the author of the internationally acclaimed books: *Why Do I Eat When I'm Not Hungry?* (Avon); and *Stop the Nightmares of Trauma* (Professional Press, USA and VAK, Germany). His latest book is *Tapping the Healer Within* with foreword by Jack Canfield, originator of the *Chicken Soup for Soul*® book series (McGraw-Hill)—which has been translated and/or made available in the United Kingdom, Japan, Korea, China, France, Taiwan, Norway, Spain, Germany, Russia and Denmark.

Dr. Callahan is a popular media personality and has treated numerous celebrity clients including Whoopi Goldberg and Kelly Ripa. Additionally, he has appeared and demonstrated Thought Field Therapy on such diverse radio and television shows as Good Morning America, The Oprah Winfrey Show, CNN, Evening Magazine, Regis Philbin, Tom Snyder, LEEZA, Jenny Jones, Phil Donahue, and Live with Regis and Kelly, as well as many others.

He is the Past President of the American Academy of Psychologists in Marital and Family Therapy and the Michigan Society of School Psychologists, Dr. Callahan has taught at the University of Michigan and Syracuse University. He was an Associate Professor at Eastern Michigan University, a Research and Clinical Psychologists at Michigan's Wayne County Training School, and he is a current Fellow of the American Academy of Psychotherapists Treating Addiction.

Dr. Callahan has had private psychotherapy practices in Detroit, New York, Los Angeles, Indian Wells, and La Quinta, California. Currently licensed in New York and California, Dr. Callahan heads the Thought Field Therapy Training Center in La Quinta, California (a Palm Springs community). The TFT Training Center conducts trainings in TFT and publishes a quarterly newsletter, *The Thought Field.*

Dr. Callahan is Chairman of the Board for the professional organization Association for Thought Field Therapy.

Joanne M. Callahan, MBA

Co-developer of Thought Field Therapy with her husband Dr. Roger Callahan, Joanne Callahan is the Chief Executive Officer of Callahan Techniques, Ltd. with worldwide headquarters located in La Quinta, California. Joanne has been the guiding force in expanding TFT into an international phenomenon with hundreds of licensed TFT practitioners providing therapeutic sessions, training and an authoritative presence in more than 80 countries around the world.

She is a graduate of the University of California Santa Barbara and received her MBA in Healthcare Administration from California State University San Marcos. Joanne is the Director of the Thought Field Therapy Training Center—and is publisher and coeditor of *The Thought Field,* an international quarterly newsletter written and distributed for TFT practitioners and clinicians.

She is trained to practice Thought Field Therapy at the Advanced and Voice Technology™ levels, and is the only person other than Dr. Roger Callahan who is certified to teach TFT at all levels. She travels the world instructing practitioners in tapping techniques and TFT diagnostic procedures.

Joanne is also the coauthor of *Thought Field Therapy and Trauma: Treatment and Theory*—and she's the coauthor of the recently revised *Stop the Nightmares of Trauma* (with foreword by Jack Canfield, originator of the *Chicken Soup for Soul*® book series). As well, she coauthored "Chapter 12, Thought Field Therapy: Aiding the Bereavement Process," in the book *Death and Trauma: The Traumatology of Grieving* (Routledge Publishers).

Joanne currently serves on the board and is an officer for the professional organization Association for Thought Field Therapy. As well, she is active in the ATFT Foundation which was formed to provide humanitarian relief, training and education worldwide. Its focus has been trauma relief in the world's most devastated areas of the globe.

Permissions

We acknowledge the many individuals who granted us permission to reprint the cited material:

Karen Piccinotti
Lisa Borg
Jenny Edwards
Jill Strunk, Ed.D. L.P
Susan Wright, PHD, MSW
Norma Gairdner, H.D.
Brian Ewart as told by Ian Graham
Lee Wells
Jo Cooper
Jenny Edwards
Guy Marriott
Suzanne M. Connolly, LCSW
Herb Ayers, MA, LMHC, TFT-Dx
Fred P. Gallo, Ph.D., author of *Energy Psychology*
Gabrielle Williamson, Australia
Lionel Mandy
David Burns
Christina Mayhew
Nora J. Baladerian, Ph.D., TFT-Adv, Lic Psychologist, Los Angeles, CA
Michelle (Miki) Butterworth
Roxane Williams
Ian Graham
Robert Grant
Dr. P. Mollon, Clinical Psychologist & Psychotherapist
D.J. Wolfaardt
Caroline A. Loose, PhD
Norma Gairdner, H.D.
Dr. Colin M. Barron
Bruce Ramsay
Dr. Victoria Yancey, Guardian Angel of Hope Connection
H.E. Hagglund, MD
Martin Law, R.Psych.
Ildiko Scurr, TFT-Adv
Nick Seferlis, M.S., LCPC, TFT-Dx
Oneyda Maestas
Dr. Victoria Yancey, Guardian Angel of Hope Connection
Christina Mayhew
Fred P. Gallo, Ph.D., author of *Energy Psychology*
Rosemarie Solarz
Michael Sills, DDS
Shad Meshad, MSW, LCSW, CTS, TFT-Dx
Stephen P. Daniel, Founder of Quantum Techniques
Caroline E. Sakai, Ph.D., TFT-VT
Dr. Colin M. Barron

Priya Pinto, Ph.D.
Robert Gairing, Ph.D.
Robert Gairing, Ph.D.
Excerpt from: *Repotting Yourself* by Mary Lou Dobbs, published by O Books
Dr. Colin M. Barron
Roopa Chari, MD., www.charicenter.com
Rosemary Wiseman, www.RosemaryWiseman.com
Ian Graham
Tom McDermott
Jenny Edwards
Dr. Colin M. Barron
Amanda Moser
Dale Solarz
Provided by Robert Pasahow, Ph.D.
Sharron Kanter, TFT-Dx
Caroline E. Sakai, Ph.D., TFT-VT
Maria Isabel Aguilar, TFT-VT, MNLP
Ron and Joyce Tate
Ildiko Scurr, TFT-Adv
Kristina Hancock
Terry Perry, TFT-Dx Practitioner, Abruzzo, Italy
Bruce N. Eimer, Ph.D., ABPP, Clinical Psychologist, www.BruceEimer.com
Shad Meshad, MSW, LCSW, CTS, TFT-Dx
Fr. Peter Mubunga Basaliza
Robert S. Harris
Caroline E. Sakai, Ph.D., TFT-VT
Nora J. Baladerian, Ph.D., TFT-Adv, Lic Psychologist, Los Angeles, CA
Marysue Hansell
Rita New, MBRCP, TFT-Dx, Cheltenham, England
Robert K. Allen. Used with permission. TFT Practitioner.
Mark Matloff, Ph.D.
Robert Paige, LCSW
Arthur R. Davis Jr., MD
James C. McAninch
Mona A. Coates
Elizabeth Niederer/ John H. Diepold, Fr., Ph.D., TFT-Dx
Fred P. Gallo, Ph.D., author of *Energy Psychology*
Robert L. Bray, PhD, LCSW, CTS, TFT-VT
Kenneth G. Kuchar-Haas
Dr. Colin M. Barron
Father Luis Jorge Gonzalez, PhD
Don Walker
Franco Manna
Dr. Dariah Morgan and Dr. Bruce R. Paton
Cathy Tanida
Dr. Victoria Yancey, Guardian Angel of Hope Connection
Mats J. Uldal
Abdulhamid Mustafa AlFirdaus
Mary L. Cowley, Ph.D., TFT-VT
Pia Cowley
Ann Marjorie Alayon, TFT-Dx

Ready to Start Tapping in Your Life?

"Tapping the Healer Within"

Using Thought Field Therapy® to Instantly Conquer Your Fears, Anxieties, and Emotional Distress.

By Roger J. Callahan, PhD,
with Richard Trubo, Forward by Dr. Earl Mindell.

The first book on "TFT" by its founder Dr. Roger Callahan. Thought Field Therapy (TFT) has already changed the way thousands of people have overcome emotional problems. Now the founder of TFT shows readers how to harness its healing power on their own, to overcome phobias, anxieties, addictions, and other common psychological problems. The process combines principles of Western and Eastern healing methods, using energy points in the body to release emotional distress.

"An invaluable tool to help the thousands of people suffering from a variety of psychological problems. Even if yours is a complex case, Dr. Callahan's method works."... *from the Foreword by Dr. Earl Mindell, author of Prescription Alternatives and Dr. Earl Mindell's Secrets of Natural Health*

You can purchase "Tapping The Healer Within" at Amazon, Barnes and Noble, most book stores, and at www.RogerCallahan.com

"Introduction to Thought Field Therapy" Self-Study Course

This new audio course package, is delivered to you online as soon as you place your order.

Get immediate access to Thought Field Therapy: Tapping Nature's Healing System course.

Online access to the audio recordings, and the Guide to Thought Field Therapy® in PDF format.

For best experience, a high speed Internet connection is required.

www.RogerCallan.com/ tft-online

Back By Popular Demand

Thought Field Therapy® Live!
A TFT Teleclass Series to learn how to apply Thought Field Therapy to your specific challenge.

Learn to Use Thought Field Therapy

Register Now

Registration details: www.RogerCallahan.com/learn-to-tap.php

Learn Objective Self-Testing to Identify and Treat Toxins and Self-Sabotage...

How much better could you feel everyday, if you could avoid eating things that make you feel bad, or, neutralize them when you eat them? What if you could eliminate negative feelings and self-sabotage when they start, or even before they happen?

The number 1 question we have been asked over the last three decades of TFT's development and training is: *How can I identify my psychological reversals and toxins my self? Or, how can I treat myself?*

We offer an all-new, one-day course to do just that. Learn to identify and self-treat the two biggest obstacles to our health and success...

Learn TFT to Help Others:
Join Us For Live Advanced 2-Day Training

Thought Field Therapy®

Boot Camp

Callahan Techniques®

The Boot Camp combines the TFT-Algo and the TFT-Dx training into a 2-day course, saving you both time and money.

This Boot Camp is hands-on training, TFT practice and live demonstrations. Attendees have the chance to work on personal issues and many experience resolution of these issues during the weekend.

Attendees receive all the materials included in the Diagnostic Training Step A and B. This material allows you to diagnose, i.e., determine the precise sequence of tapping required, to quickly help most psychological problems and daily stresses.

You can receive both the algorithm and diagnostic level certifications from this single course. CE's are also available.

Join us at a TFT Boot Camp Near You:
www.RogerCallahan.com/bootcamp

"Get a One-On-One TFT Consultation"

We Now Provide Private Consultations For Thought Field Therapy Treatment.

TFT is a highly effective, non-invasive, healthy self-help alternative to long-term, or drug related psychotherapy.

Dr. Callahan has demonstrated it on CNN, Regis & Kelly, LEEZA, Oprah, and other television and radio shows world-wide.

He believes TFT can have a significant impact on the decrease of human suffering and;

- Rapid trauma relief
- Overcome grief, depression and heart rate variability
- Eliminate fears, anxiety and stress
- Successful weight loss or smoking cessation
- Ease the weight of depression without medications

If you want to use TFT to improve your health, or are feeling overwhelmed by stress or grief, have fears that are impacting your life, or want to beat an addiction... we'll show you how TFT can help.

To arrange for your private TFT consultation to help you overcome your specific challenges, please fill out the form located at our website below and we'll contact you to discuss how TFT can help you overcome your specific problem or challenge.

www.RogerCallahan.com/specials.php or call 760-564-1008